CHENG & TSUI

"Bringing Asia to the World"™

中文听说读写 · 中文聽說讀寫

INTEGRATED CHINESE

Simplified and Traditional Characters

2

Character Workbook

4th Edition

Yuehua Liu and Tao-chung Yao
Nyan-Ping Bi, Yaohua Shi, Liangyan Ge

Original Edition by Tao-chung Yao and Yuehua Liu
Yea-fen Chen, Liangyan Ge, Nyan-Ping Bi, Xiaojun Wang, Yaohua Shi

CHENG & TSUI

"Bringing Asia to the World"™

Copyright © 2018, 2009, 2005, 1997 by
Cheng & Tsui Company, Inc.

Fourth Edition 2018

23 22 21 20 19   2 3 4 5

ISBN 978-1-62291-144-8 [Fourth Edition]

Printed in the United States of America

The *Integrated Chinese* series includes
textbooks, workbooks, character
workbooks, teacher's resources, audio,
video, and more. Visit chengtsui.co
for more information on the other
components of *Integrated Chinese*.

Publisher
JILL CHENG

Editorial Manager
BEN SHRAGGE

Editor
LEI WANG

Creative Director
CHRISTIAN SABOGAL

Interior Design
KATE PAPADAKI

Cheng & Tsui Company, Inc.
Phone (617) 988-2400 / (800) 554-1963
Fax (617) 426-3669
25 West Street
Boston, MA 02111-1213 USA
chengtsui.co

Contents

Preface

This completely revised and redesigned Character Workbook is meant to accompany the Fourth Edition of *Integrated Chinese* (IC). It has been about twenty years since the IC series came into existence in 1997. During these years, amid all the historical changes that have taken place in China and the rest of the world, the demand for Chinese language teaching/learning materials has grown dramatically. We are greatly encouraged by the fact that IC not only has been a widely used textbook at the college level all over the United States and beyond, but also has become increasingly popular for advanced language students in high schools. Based on user feedback, we have made numerous changes so that the Character Workbook can become an even more useful tool for students of Chinese.

Stressing the importance of learning a new character by its components

Learning a new character becomes much easier if the student can identify its components. The student should learn how to write the forty radicals at the beginning of the Volume 1 Character Workbook in the correct stroke order first, because these forty radicals will appear repeatedly in other characters later. If a new character contains a component already familiar to the student, the stroke order of that component will not be introduced again. However, we will show the stroke order of all new components as they appear when we introduce new characters. For example, when we introduce the character 孩 *(hái)* (child) in Lesson 2, Volume 1, we do not show the stroke order for the radical 子 *(zǐ)* (child) because 子 already appeared in the radical section. Therefore, we only display the stroke order for the other component 亥 *(hài)* (the last of the Twelve Earthly Branches). For the same reason, when 亥 appears in the new character 刻 *(kè)* (quarter of an hour) in Lesson 3, Volume 1, its stroke order is not displayed. When the student learns a new character, he or she can easily tell if a component in the character has appeared in previous lessons. If the stroke order for that component is not displayed, it means that the component is not new. The student should try to recall where he or she has seen it before. By doing so, the student can connect new characters with old ones and build up a character bank. We believe that learning by association will help the student memorize characters more effectively.

Main features of the new Character Workbook

a. Both simplified and traditional characters are introduced
If a character appears in both simplified and traditional form, we show both to accommodate different learner needs. In this volume, to reflect the predominance of simplified characters in Chinese language instruction, we have listed simplified characters first.

b. Pinyin and English definition are clearly noted
We have moved the *pinyin* and the English definition above each character for easy recognition and review.

c. Radicals are highlighted
The radical of each character is highlighted. Knowing what radical group a character belongs to is essential when looking up that character in a traditional dictionary in which the characters are arranged according to their radicals. To a certain extent, radicals can also help the student decipher the meaning of a character. For example, characters containing the radical 贝 / 貝 *(bèi)* (shell), such as 贵 / 貴 *(guì)* (expensive), and 货 / 貨 *(huò)* (merchandise), are often associated with money or value. The student can group the characters sharing the same radical together and learn them by association.

d. Stroke order is prominently displayed
Another important feature is the numbering of each stroke in the order of its appearance. Each number is marked at the beginning of that particular stroke. We firmly believe that it is essential to write a character in the correct stroke order, and to know where each stroke begins and ends. To display the

stroke order more prominently, we have moved the step-by-step character writing demonstration next to the main characters.

e. "Training wheels" are provided
We also provide grids with fine shaded lines inside to help the student better envision and balance their characters when practicing.

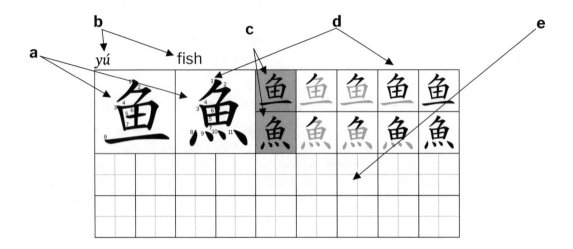

Other changes

In response to user feedback, we have updated the traditional characters to ensure they match the standard set currently used in Taiwan. For reference, we have consulted the Taiwan Ministry of Education's Revised Chinese Dictionary. This change has been overseen by the editors.

In order to focus on character recognition and acquisition, we decided not to include elements having to do with phonetic identification and phrase recognition.

To help the student look up characters more easily, we decided to limit the indices to two: one arranged alphabetically by *pinyin* and the other by lesson. Additional appendices that are not directly linked to the practice of writing characters, such as the English-Chinese glossary, are available in the Textbook.

The formation of the radicals in this book is based on the Modern Chinese Dictionary (现代汉语词典/ 現代漢語詞典) published by the Commercial Press (商务印书馆/商務印書館). A total of 201 radicals appear in that dictionary, and in some cases the same character is listed under more than one radical. For the characters in this book that fall in that category, we provide two radicals in order to facilitate students' dictionary searches. The two radicals are presented in order from top to bottom (e.g., 名: 夕, 口), left to right (e.g., 功: 工, 力), and large to small (e.g., 章: 音, 立; 麻: 麻, 广).

The changes that we made in the new version reflect the collective wishes of the users. We would like to take this opportunity to thank those who gave us feedback on how to improve the Character Workbook. We would like to acknowledge in particular Professor Hu Shuangbao of Peking University and Professor Shi Dingguo of Beijing Language and Culture University, both of whom read the entire manuscript and offered invaluable comments and suggestions for revision.

Note: Prefaces to the previous editions of IC are available at chengtsui.co.

Lesson 11: Weather

Dialogue 1: Tomorrow's Weather Will Be Even Better!

bǐ compared with (comparison marker), to compare

比 比 比 比 比 比

xuě snow

雪 雪 雪 雪 雪 雪

yuán garden

园 園 元 园 园 园 园
袁 園 園 園 園 園 園 園 園

huá slippery; to slide

滑 滑 滑 滑 滑 滑 滑 滑
滑 滑 滑 滑 滑 滑 滑 滑

bīng   ice

冰   冰冰冰

lěng   cold

冷   冷冷冷冷冷冷

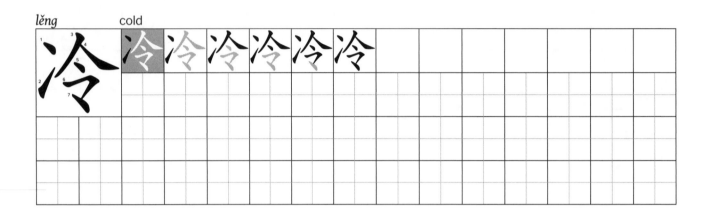

gāng   just now, a moment ago

刚 剛   刚 刚 刚 刚 刚 刚
   剛 剛 剛 剛 剛 剛 剛 剛 剛 剛

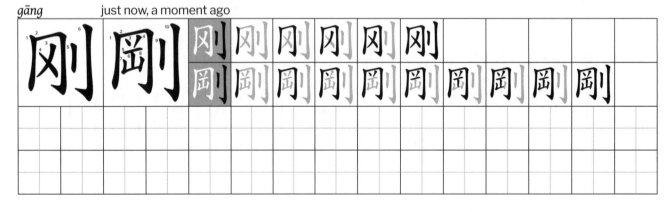

bào   newspaper; to report

报 報   报 报 报 报 报 报
   報 報 報 報 報 報 報 報 報

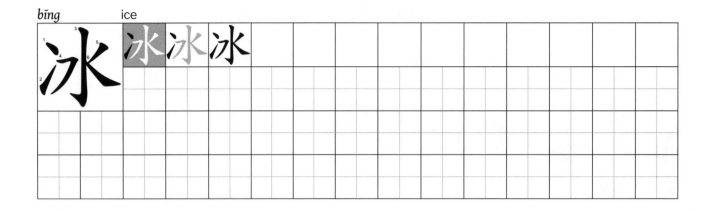

gèng　　even more

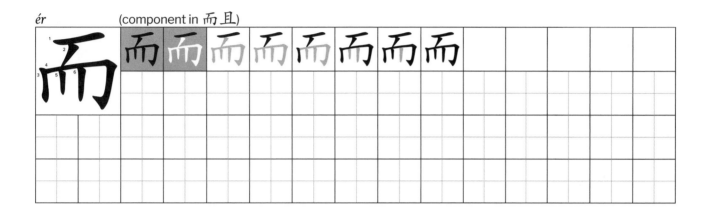

ér　　(component in 而且)

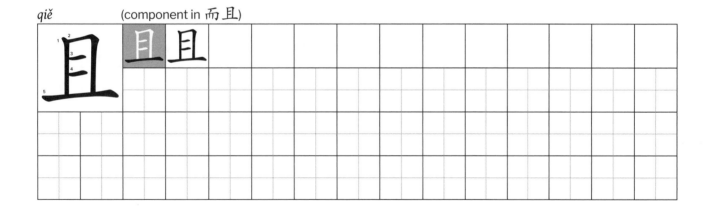

qiě　　(component in 而且)

且 且

nuǎn　　warm

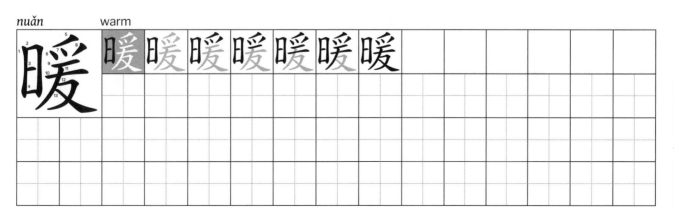

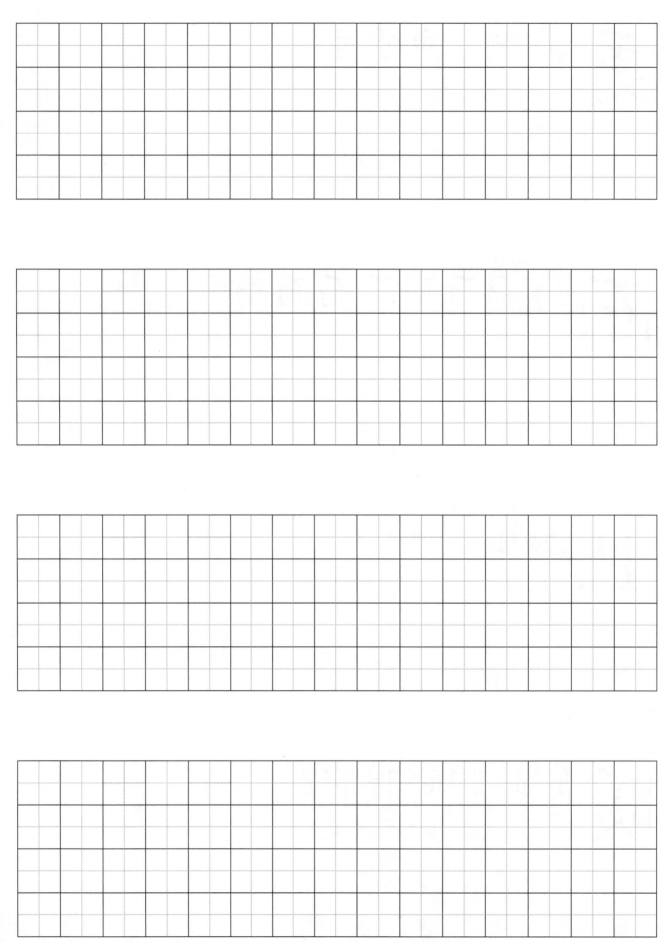

Dialogue 2: The Weather Here Is Awful!

fēi not, non-

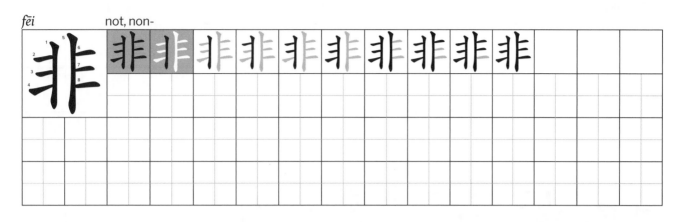

zāo rotten, decayed

gāo cake

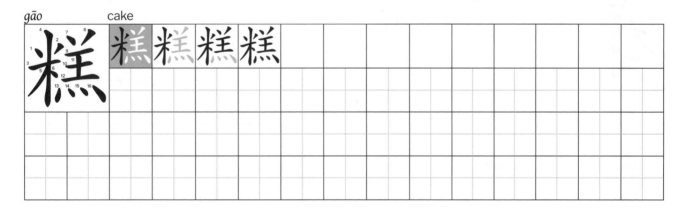

dōng winter

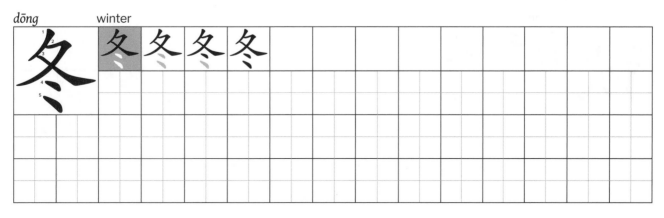

xià　summer

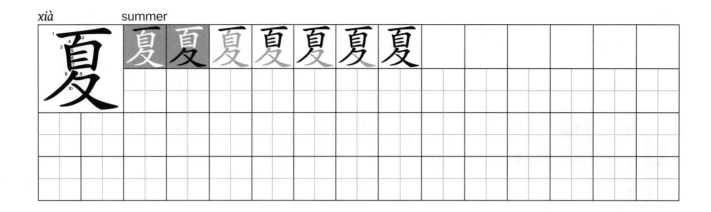

rè　hot

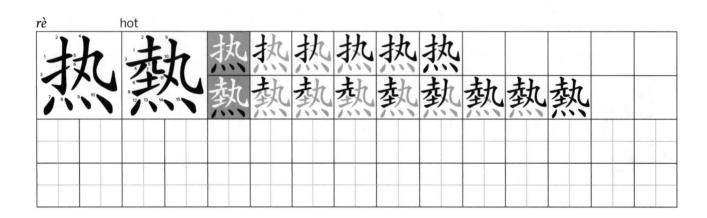

chūn　spring

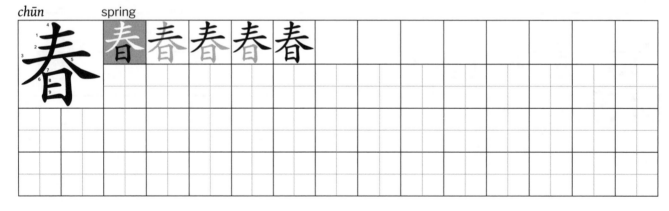

qiū　autumn, fall

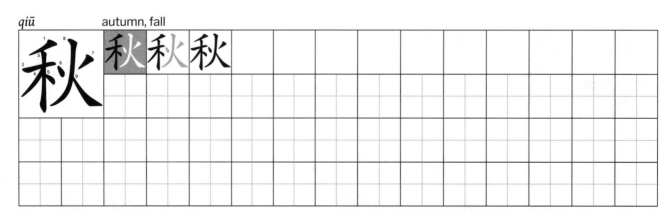

shū　to relax; comfortable

舒 舒 舒 舒 舒

Characters from Proper Nouns

jiā　to add

加 加 加 加 加

zhōu　state

州 州 州 州 州 州 州 州

Lesson 12: Dining

xiàng   likeness, portrait

像 像 | 像像像像像像像像像像
像像
像像像像像像像像像像
像像像

wù   affair, task

务 務 | 务务务务务务
務務務務務務務務

zhuō   table

桌 | 桌桌桌桌桌桌

pán   plate, dish

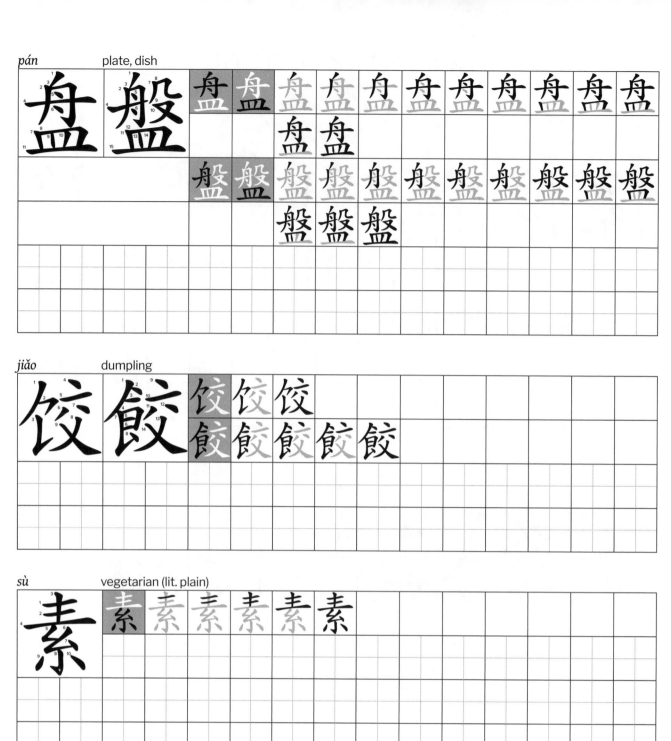

jiǎo   dumpling

sù   vegetarian (lit. plain)

dòu   bean

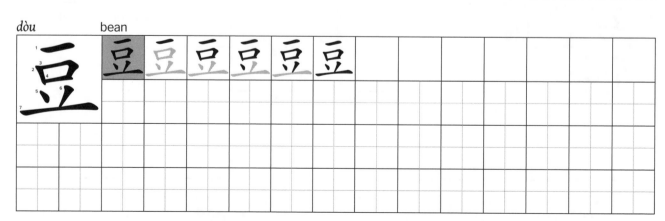

fǔ   rotten; turn bad

腐　腐 腐 腐 腐 腐 腐

fàng   to put, to place

放　放 放 放 放

ròu   meat

肉　肉 肉 肉

wǎn   bowl

碗　碗 碗 碗 碗 碗 碗 碗 碗 碗

suān　　　　　sour

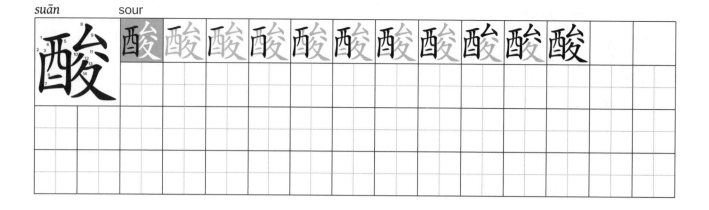

酸　酸 酸 酸 酸 酸 酸 酸 酸 酸 酸

là　　　　　spicy, hot

辣　辣 辣 辣 辣 辣

tāng　　　　　soup

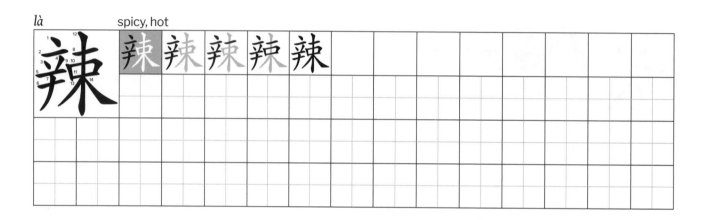

汤 湯　汤 汤 汤 汤 汤
　　　　湯 湯 湯 湯 湯 湯 湯 湯

wèi　　　　　flavor, taste

味　味 味 味 味

jīng　　essence; refined

精　精 精 精 精 精 精 精

yán　　salt

盐　鹽　盐 盐 盐 盐
　　　鹽 鹽 鹽 鹽 鹽 鹽 鹽 鹽 鹽 鹽
　　　鹽 鹽 鹽 鹽 鹽 鹽 鹽 鹽 鹽 鹽

mài　　to sell

卖　賣　卖 卖 卖 卖
　　　賣 賣 賣 賣 賣

wán　　finished

完　完 完 完

qīng　　　blue, green

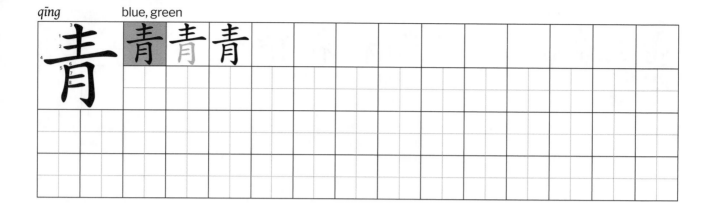

kě　　　thirsty

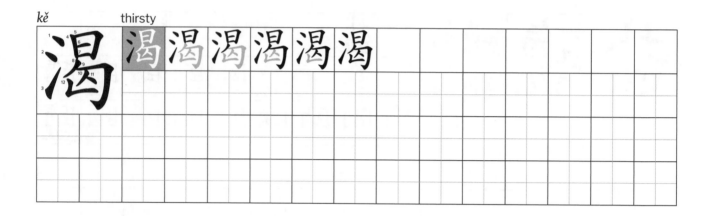

xiē　　　(measure word for an indefinite amount), some

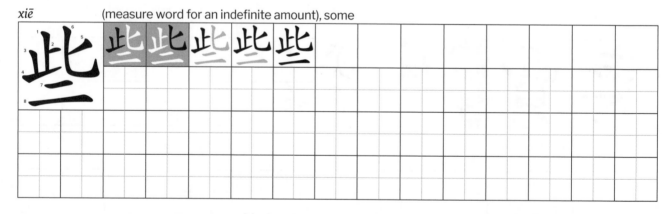

gòu　　　enough

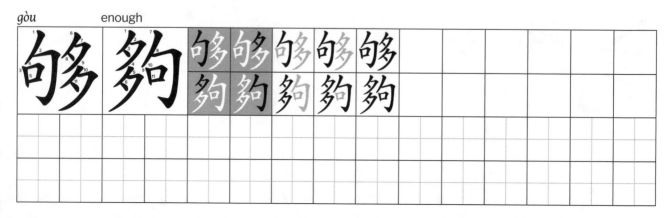

è   hungry

饿 餓 饿 饿 饿
　　　　饿 餓 餓

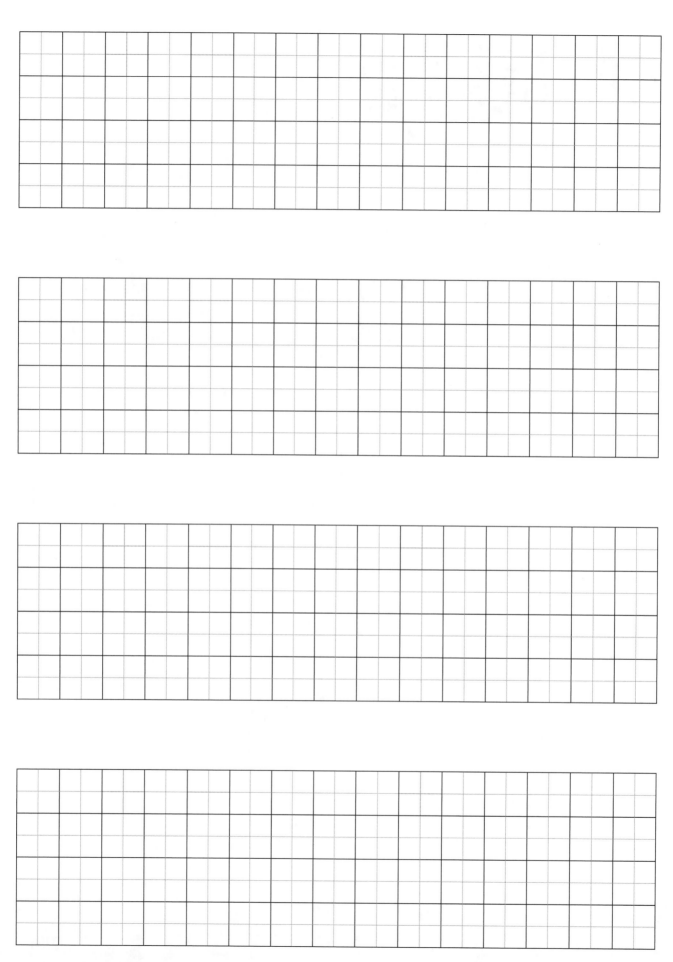

fù teacher, instructor

傅 傅傅傅傅傅傅傅傅

táng sugar

糖 糖糖糖糖糖糖糖糖

cù vinegar

醋 醋醋醋醋

yú fish

鱼 鱼 鱼鱼鱼鱼鱼

tián sweet

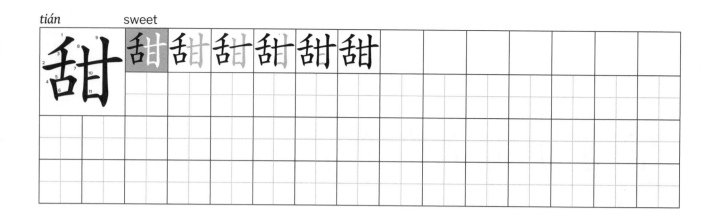

jí extremely

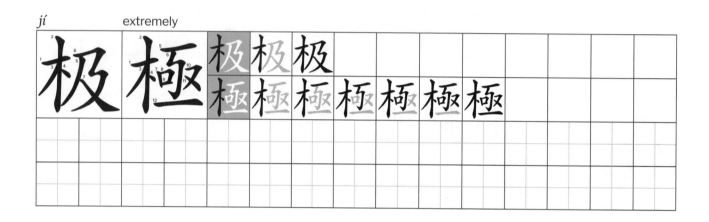

shāo to burn

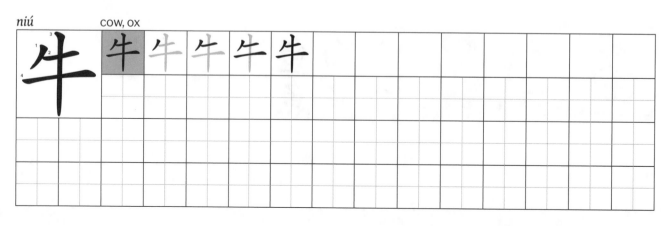

niú cow, ox

liáng　　cool

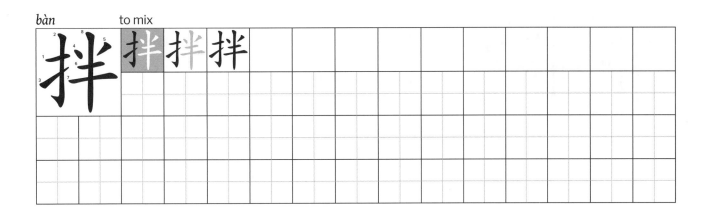

bàn　　to mix

guā　　melon, gourd

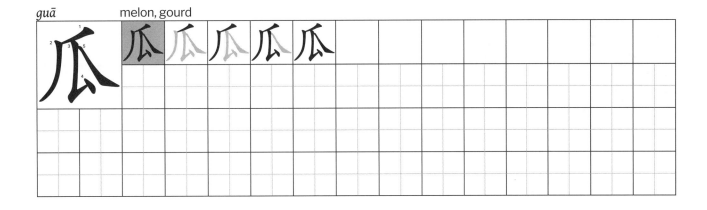

mǐ　　uncooked rice

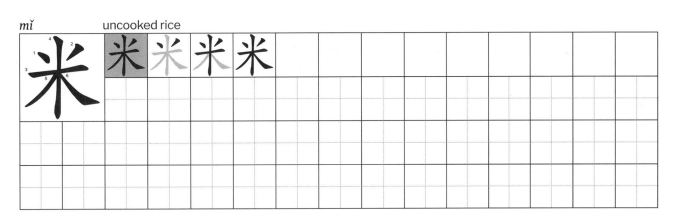

wàng to forget

忘

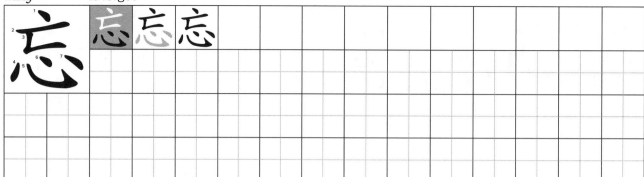

dài to bring, to take, to carry, to come with

带 带

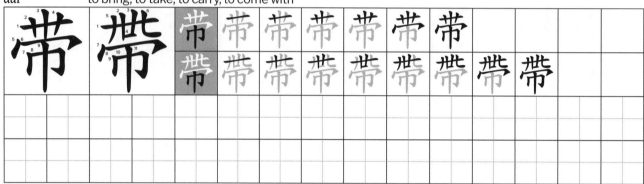

qīng pure, clear

清

清 清 清

chǔ neat

楚

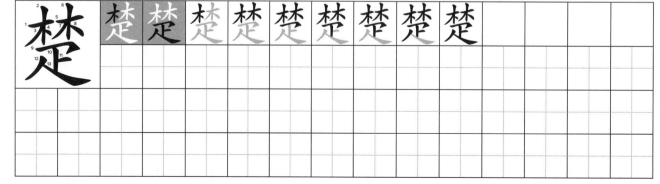

guān   to involve, to close

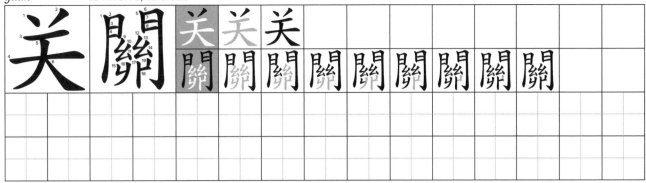

xì   to relate to

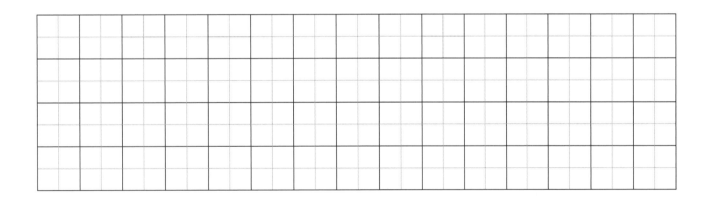

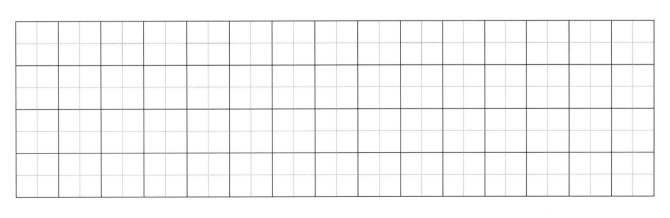

Lesson 13: Asking Directions

Dialogue 1: Where Are You Off To?

yùn   to move

运 運 运 运 运 运 运
運 運 運 運

dòng   to move

动 動 动 动 动 动
動 動 動

páng   side, edge

旁 旁 旁 旁 旁 旁 旁

yuǎn   far

远 遠 远 远 远
遠 遠 遠

lí　　　away from

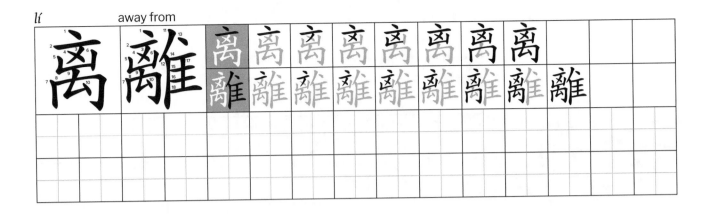

huó　　　to live; living

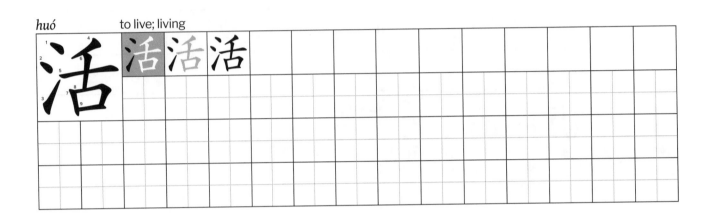

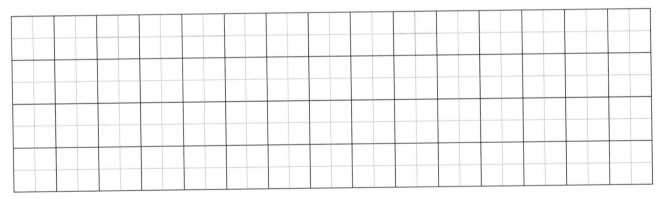

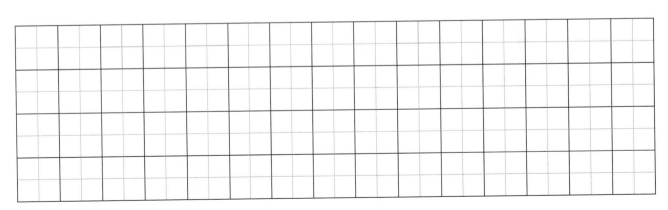

ná　　　to take, to get

拿　拿　拿　合　拿

cì　　　(measure word for frequency)

次　次　次　次

cóng　　　from

从　從　从　从　从
　　　從　從　從　從　從　從　從

zhí　　　straight

直　直　直

wǎng towards

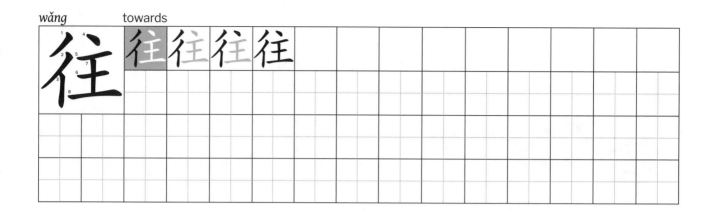

nán south

南

guǎi to turn

拐

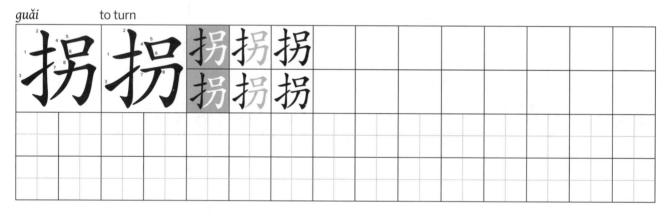

āi (exclamatory particle to express surprise or dissatisfaction)

哎 哎

dēng light

灯 燈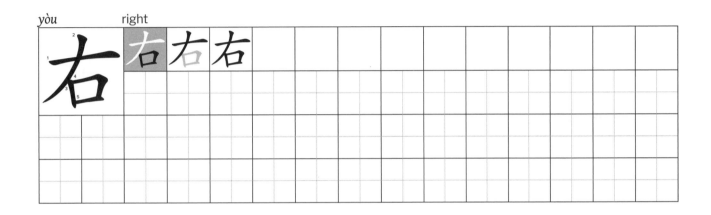

yòu right

右

zuǒ left

左

gǔ grain, valley

谷

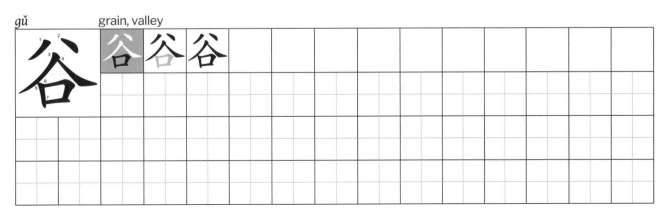

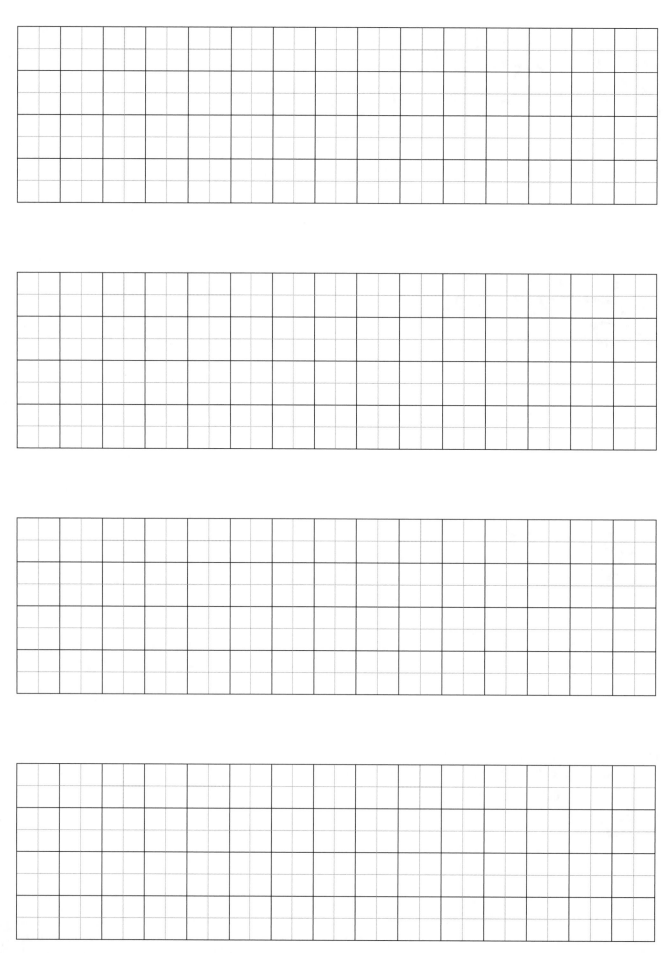

Lesson 14: Birthday Party

Dialogue 1: Let's Go to a Party!

biǎo (component in 表姐)

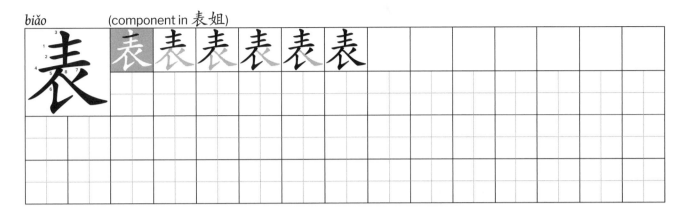

lǐ gift, ceremony

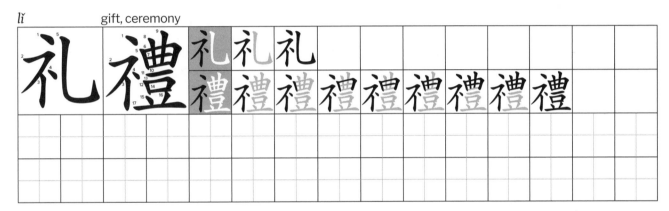

wù thing, matter

物 物 物 物 物 物

běn (measure word for books)

本 本 本

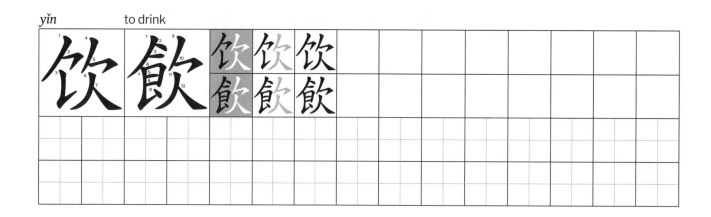

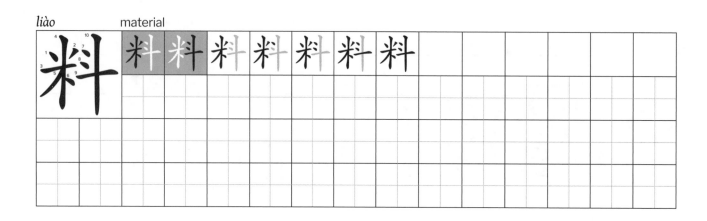

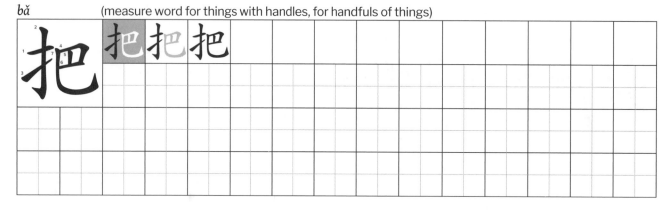

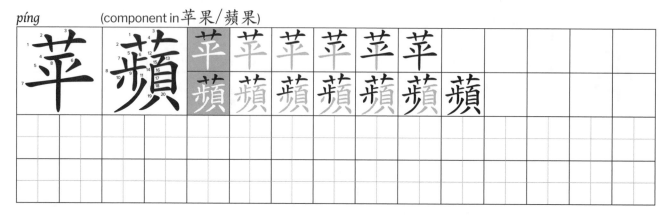

lí　　pear

梨　梨 梨 梨 梨

zhù　　to live (in a certain place)

住　住 住 住

zhòng　　heavy, serious

重　重 重 重 重 重 重 重 重

jiē　　to catch, to meet, to welcome

接　接 接 接 接

lóu multi-story building, floor (of a multi-level building)

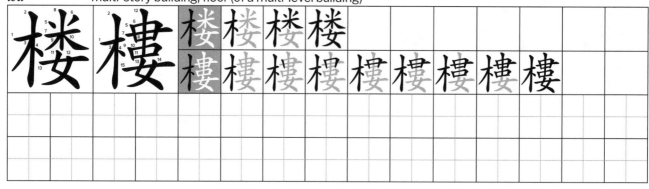

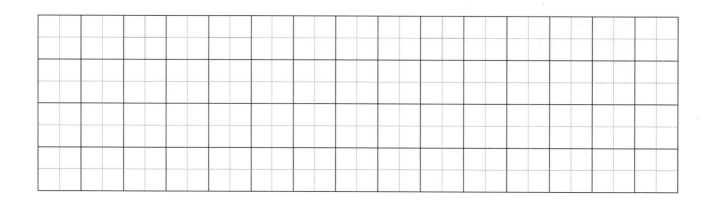

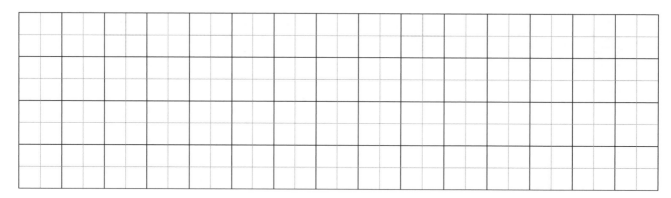

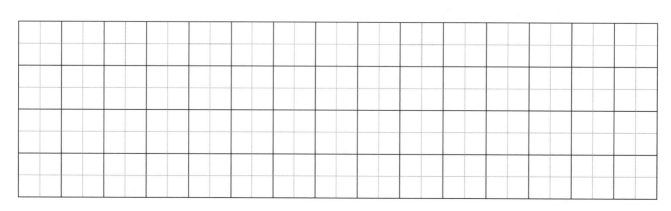

Dialogue 2: Birthday Bash

zhōng   clock

钟 鐘 钟钟钟 鐘鐘鐘鐘

tóu   head

头 頭 头头头头头头 頭頭頭

cōng   able to hear well

聪 聰 聪聪聪聪聪 聰聰聰聰聰聰聰

shǔ   heat

暑 暑暑暑

bān　　class

班

shǔ　　to belong to

属　屬

gǒu　　dog

狗

liǎn　　face

脸　臉

yuán round

圆 圆 员 圆 圆 圆 圆
員 圓 圓 圓 圓

yǎn eye

眼 眼 眼 眼

jīng eyeball

睛 睛 睛 睛

bí nose

鼻 鼻 鼻 鼻 鼻 鼻 鼻

zuǐ mouth

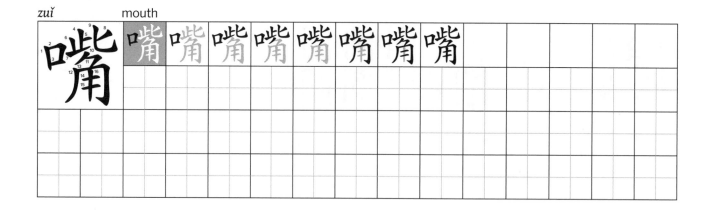

dìng settled, decided

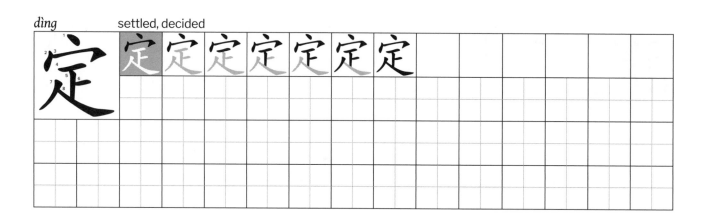

dàn egg

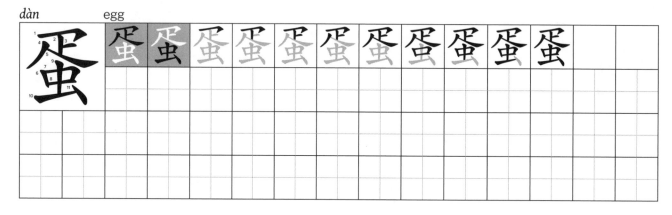

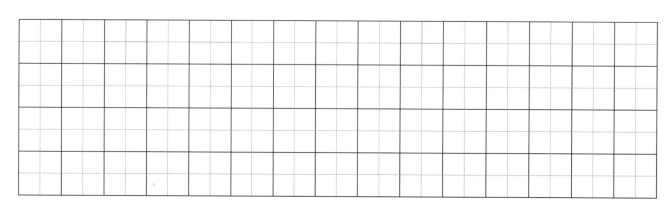

lún　　　ethics, moral principles

伦　倫　伦 伦 伦 伦
　　　倫 倫 倫 倫 倫 倫 倫 倫

mǔ　　　housemaid

姆　姆 姆 姆 姆 姆 姆

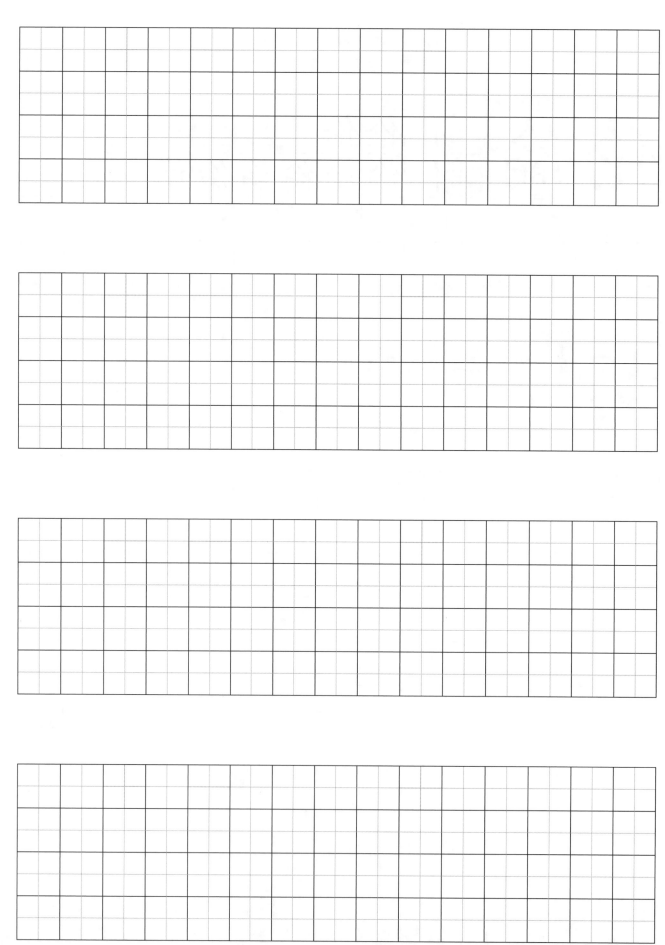

Lesson 15: Seeing a Doctor

Dialogue 1: My Stomach Is Killing Me!

bìng   illness; to become ill

病 病 病 病 病 病 病

yuàn   yard, compound

院 院 院 院 院
             院 院 院

dù   belly, abdomen, stomach

肚 肚 肚 肚

téng   to ache

疼 疼 疼 疼

sǐ   to die; (a complement indicating an extreme degree)

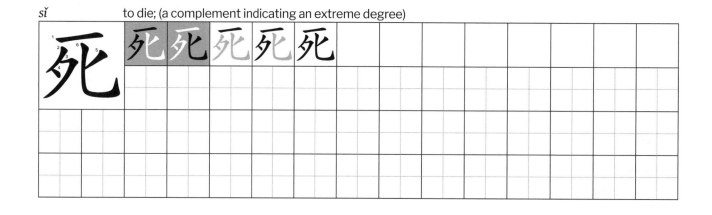

yè   night

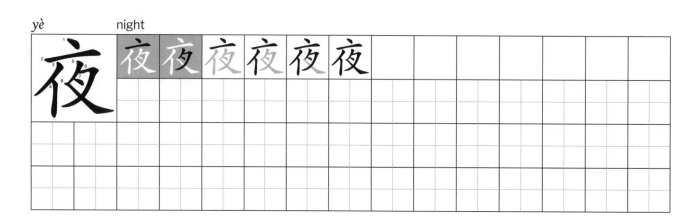

cè   toilet, restroom

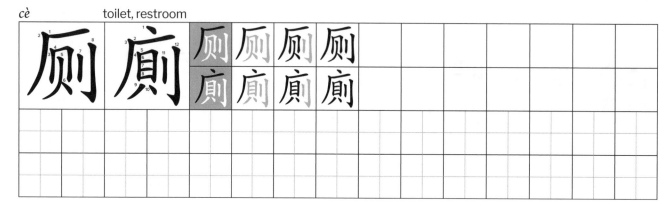

xiāng   box, case

箱

tǎng   to lie, to recline

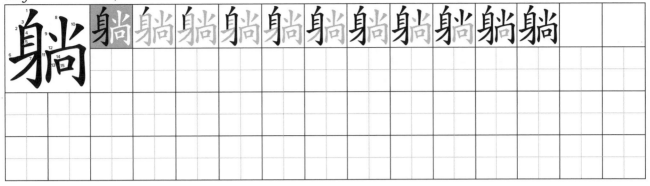

jiǎn   to inspect, to examine

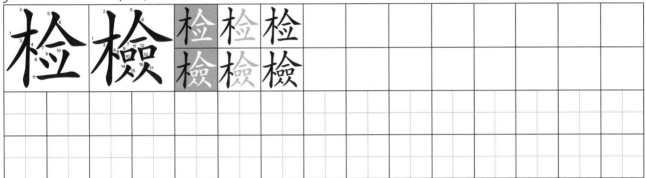

chá   to look up

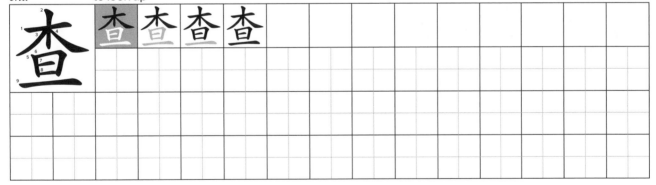

huài   bad

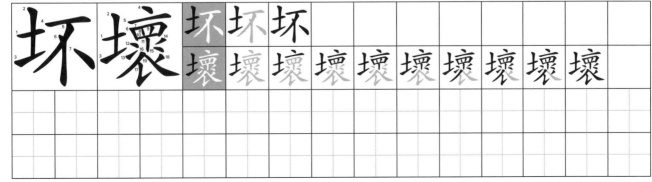

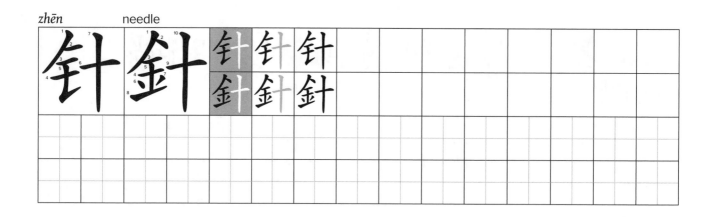

zhēn   needle

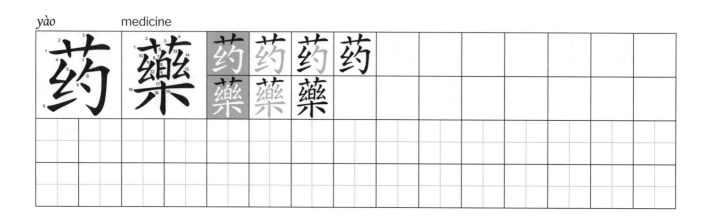

yào   medicine

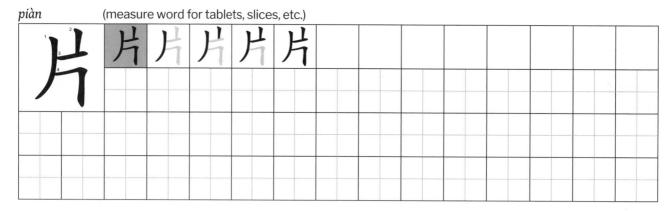

piàn   (measure word for tablets, slices, etc.)

biàn   (measure word for complete courses of an action or instances of an action)

gǎn　　to feel, to sense

感　感 感 感 感 感 感 感 感 感

mào　　to belch, to emit

冒　冒 冒 冒

shēn　　body

身　身 身

tǐ　　body

体 體　体 体 体
　　　　體 體 體

yǎng itchy

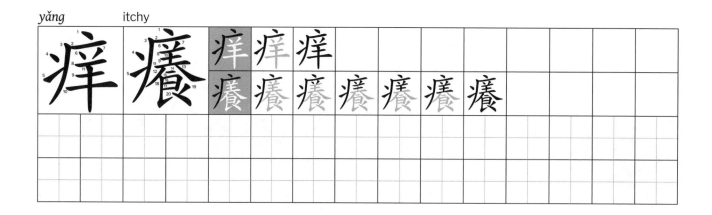

mǐn nimble, agile

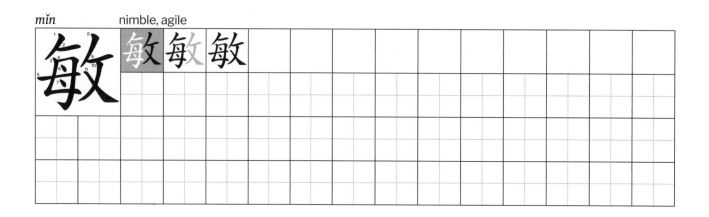

jiàn healthy

kāng healthy, affluent

bǎo   insurance; to protect

保 保保保保

xiǎn   risk, danger

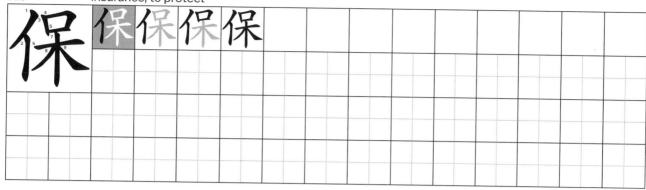

gǎn   to rush

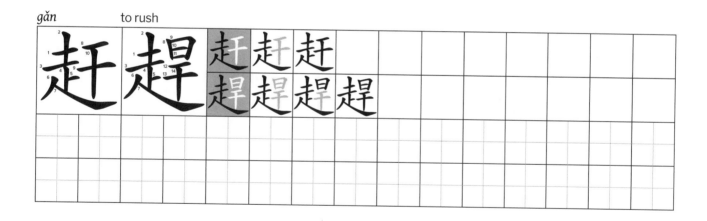

yuè   to exceed

越 越越越越越越越

xiū to cease

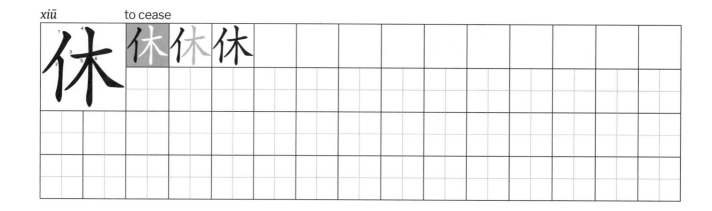

xī to cease

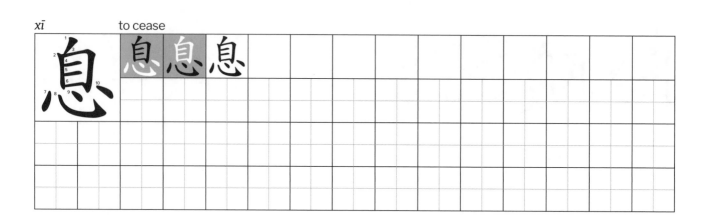

lǎn lazy

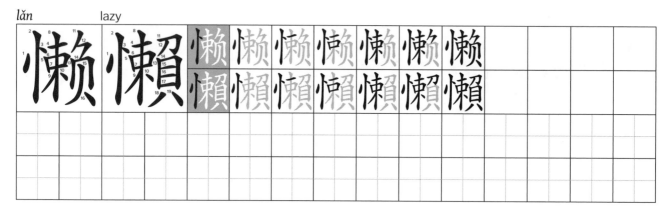

luàn randomly, arbitrarily, messily

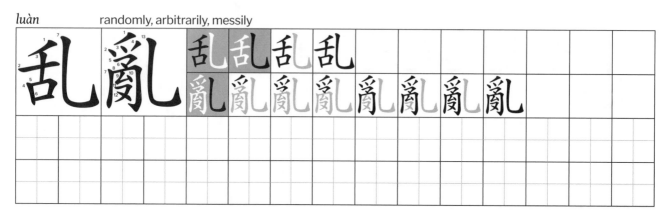

Lesson 16: Dating

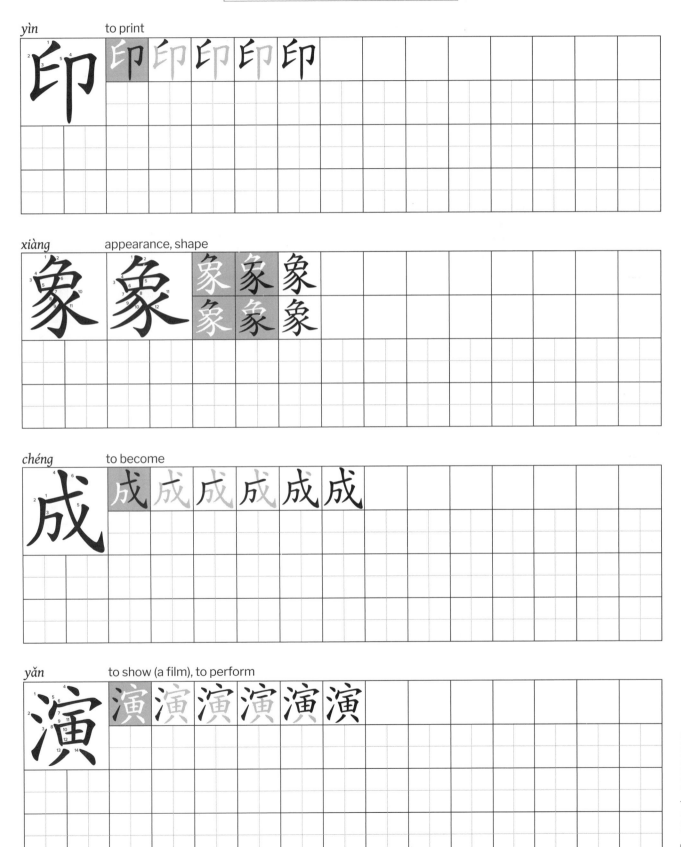

yìn   to print

印 印 印 印 印 印

xiàng   appearance, shape

象 象 象 象 象
象 象 象

chéng   to become

成 成 成 成 成 成

yǎn   to show (a film), to perform

演 演 演 演 演 演

fèi   to spend, to take (effort)

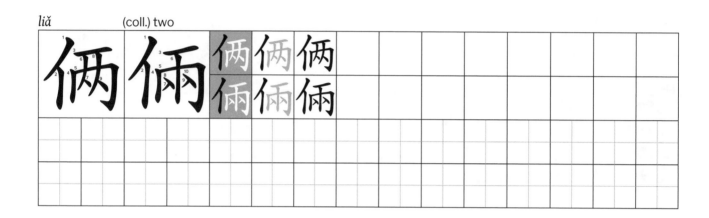

liǎ   (coll.) two

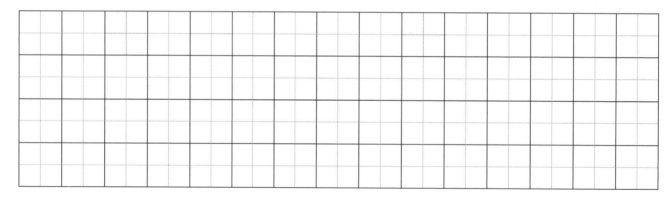

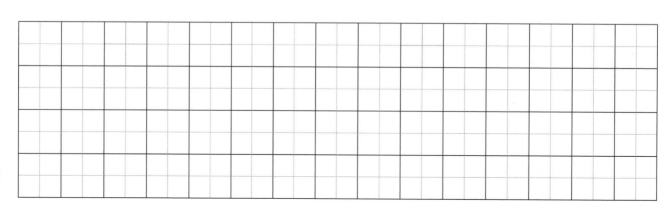

jì　　to remember

记　記　记　记　记
　　　　記　記　記

mǎ　　(symbol indicating a number)

码　碼　码　码　码
　　　　碼　碼　碼

bān　　to move

搬　搬　搬　搬　搬

sǎo　　to sweep

扫　掃　扫　扫　扫
　　　　掃　掃　掃　掃　掃　掃

zhěng to put in order

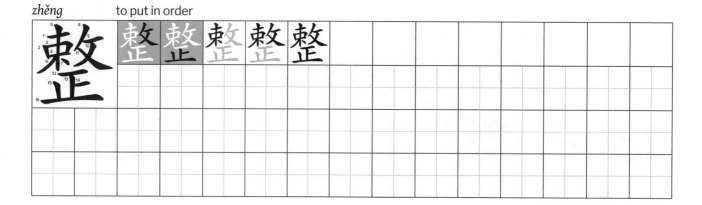

lǐ reason; in good order

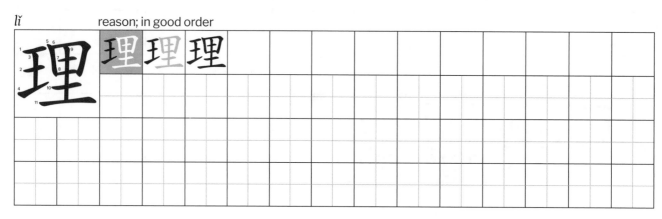

fáng house

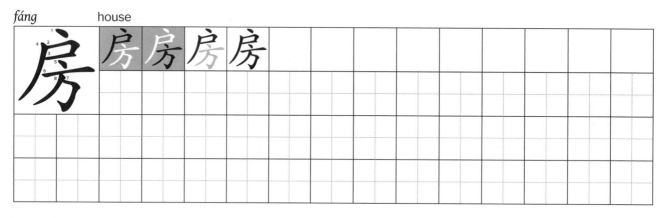

lǚ to travel

Lesson 17: Renting an Apartment

chǎo   to quarrel; noisy

吵   吵 吵 吵

lián   even

连 連   连 连 连 / 連 連 連

guǎng   wide, vast

广 廣   广 广 广 广 / 廣 廣 廣 廣 廣

fù   to attach; near

附 附   附 附 附 附 / 附 附 附 附

tào (measure word for things that come in a set or sets)

套 套套套套套套套

yù dwelling, residence

寓 寓寓寓寓寓寓寓

wò to lie (down)

卧 臥 臥臥臥臥臥臥臥臥

chú kitchen

厨 廚 厨厨厨厨廚廚廚廚

wèi　　to guard, to protect

jiā　　家: family, home; 傢: furniture

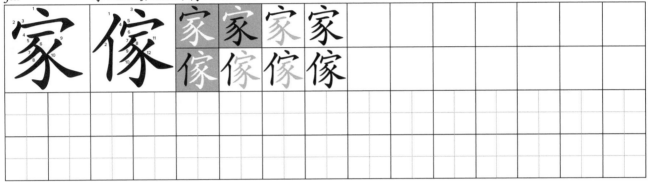

jù　　具: tool, utensil; 俱: all, complete; altogether

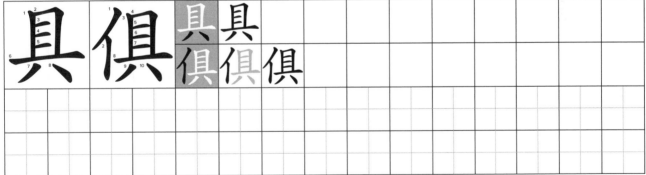

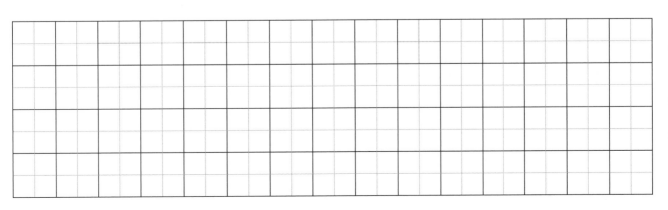

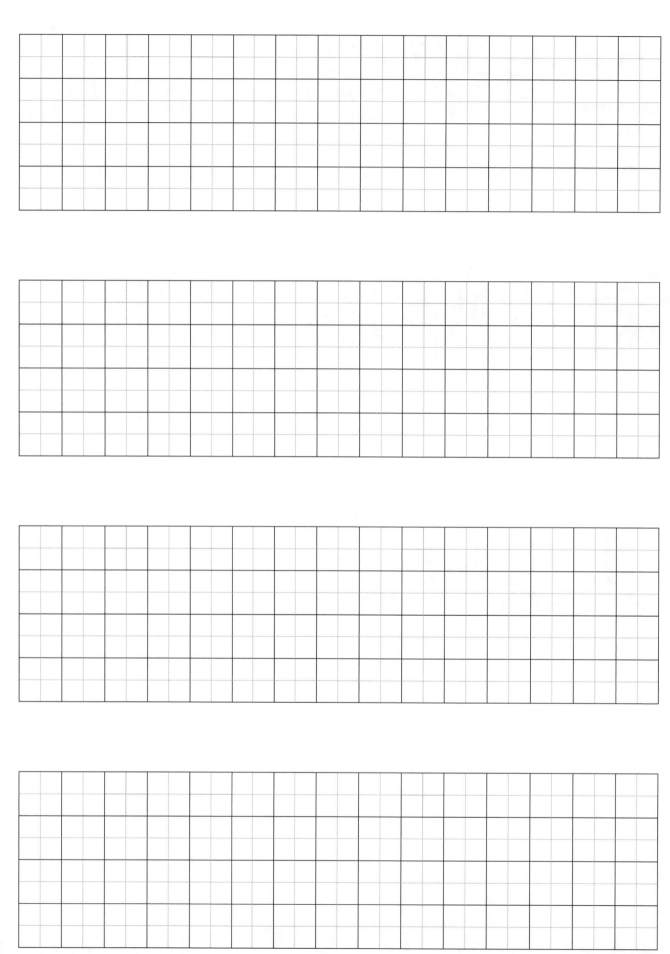

gān dry

干 乾 干 干 干 干 干
乾 乾 乾 乾 乾 乾

jìng clean

净 淨 净 净 净 净 净 净
淨 淨 淨 淨 淨 淨

shā sand

沙 沙 沙 沙

yǐ chair

椅 椅 椅 椅

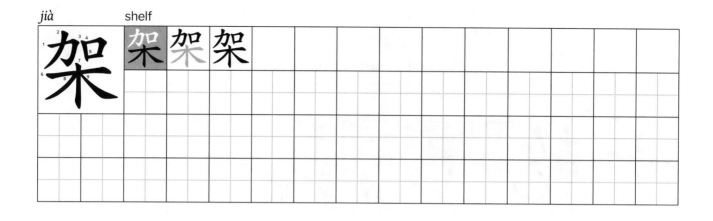

jià   shelf

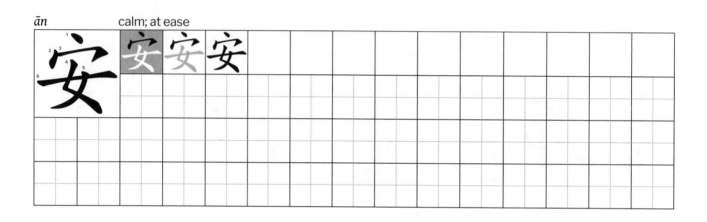

ān   calm; at ease

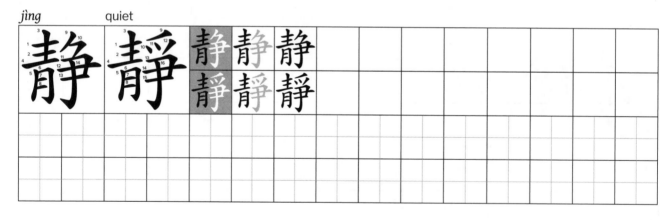

jìng   quiet

yuán   (measure word for the basic Chinese monetary unit), yuan

mín   the people

民 民民民民民民

bì   currency

幣 幣
币 幣 币 币 币 币
幣 幣 幣 幣 幣

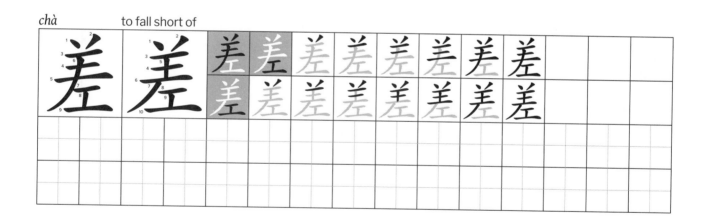

chà   to fall short of

差 差 差 差 差 差 差 差 差
差 差 差 差 差 差 差 差

yā   to give as security

押 押 押 押 押

dāng to serve as, to be

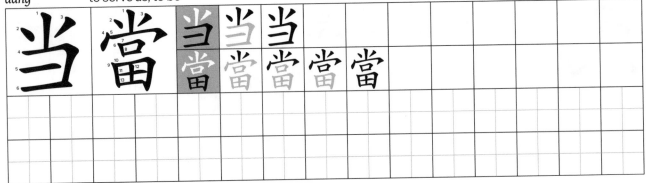

lìng other, another

另

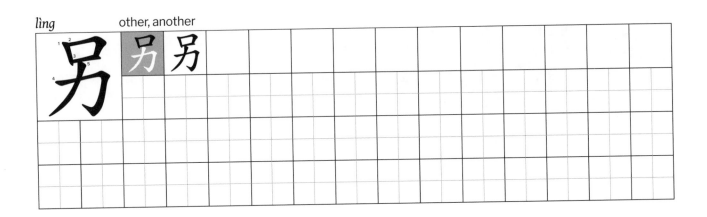

zhǔn to allow, to be allowed

准

yǎng to raise

养

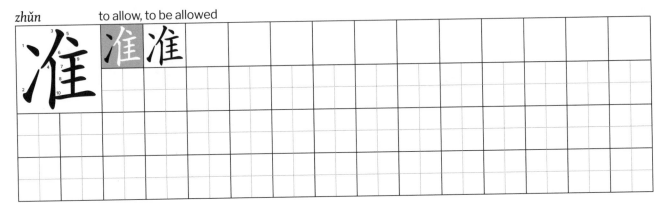

chǒng   to dote on, to pamper

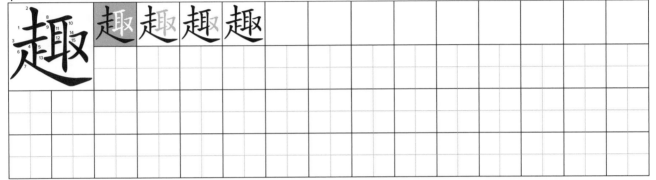

qù   interest, delight, aspiration

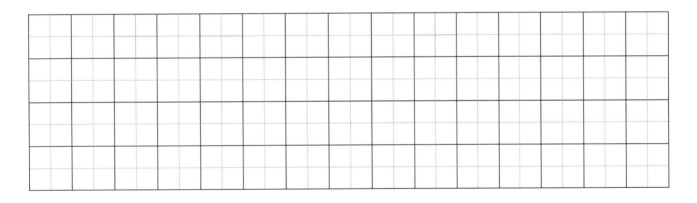

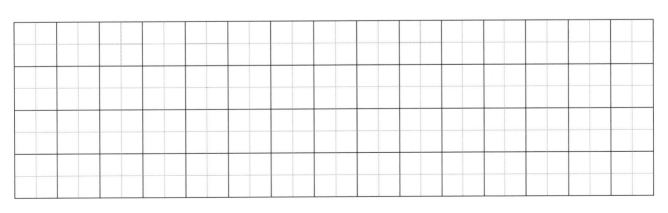

Lesson 18: Sports

Dialogue 1: Getting in Shape

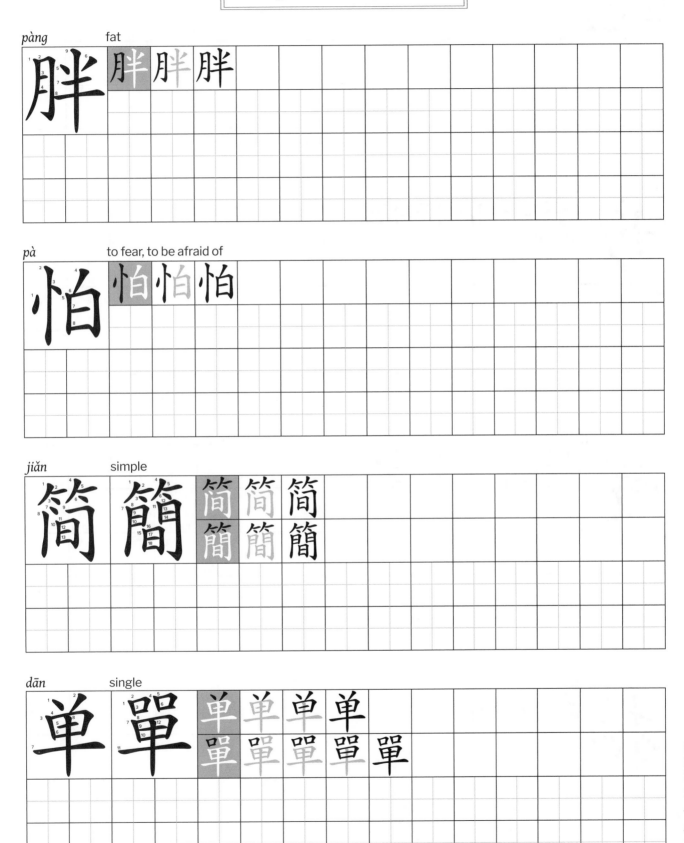

pàng fat

pà to fear, to be afraid of

jiǎn simple

dān single

pǎo　　to run

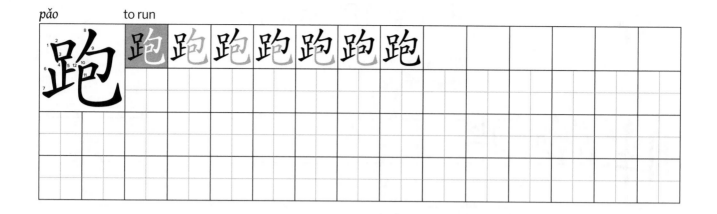

bù　　step, pace

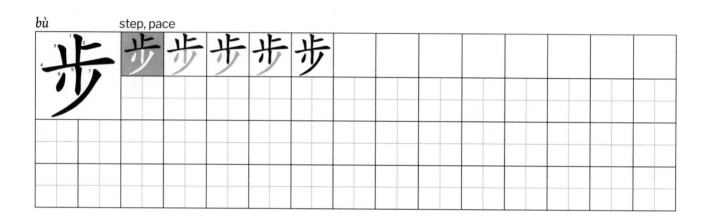

shòu　　to bear

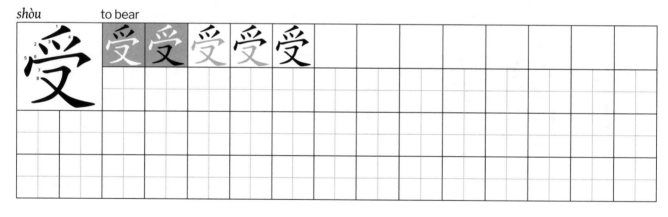

pāi　　racket

lán   basket

yóu   to swim, to rove around

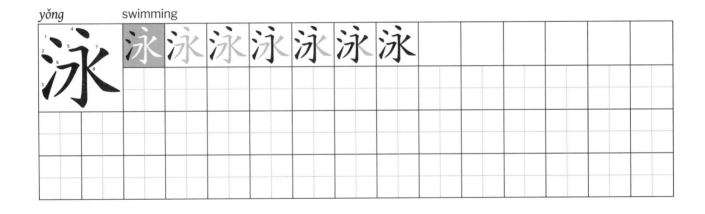

yǒng   swimming

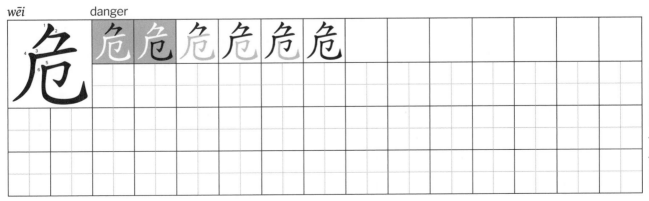

wēi   danger

yān   to submerge

淹

yuàn   wish, hope

愿 願

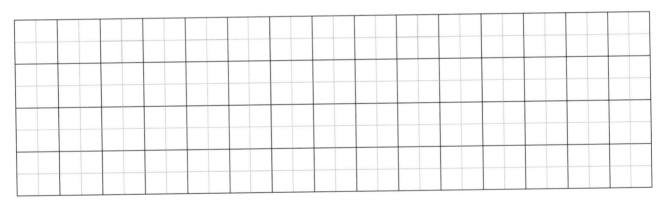

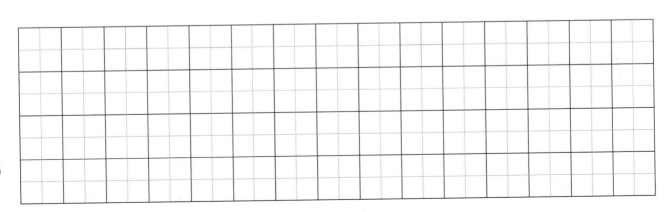

Dialogue 2: Watching American Football

tí   to lift

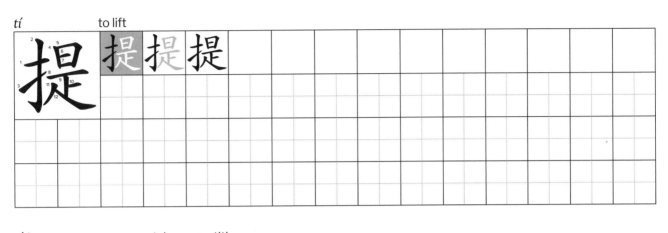

sài   game, match, competition

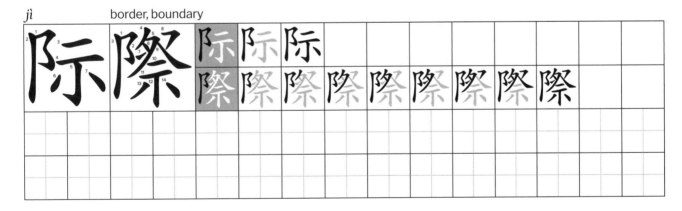

jì   border, boundary

shì   type, style

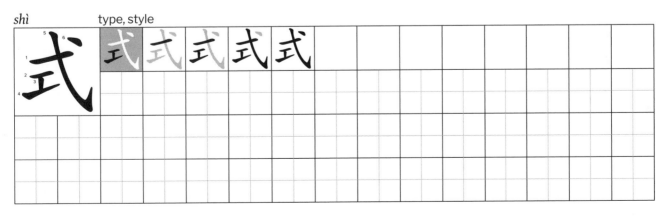

yīng   should, ought to

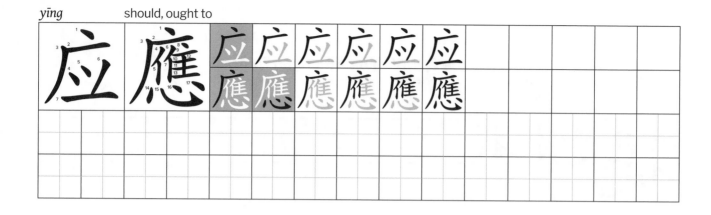

gāi   should, ought to

jiǎo   foot

脚 腳

tī   to kick

踢

bào   to hold or carry in the arms

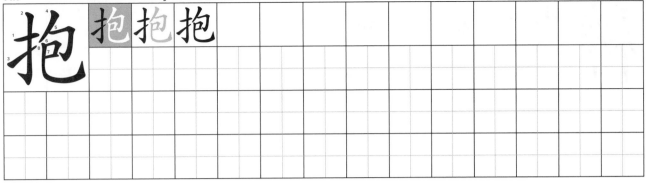

yā   to press, to hold down, to weigh down

bèi   by

被

dān   to be burdened with

bàng   fantastic, super

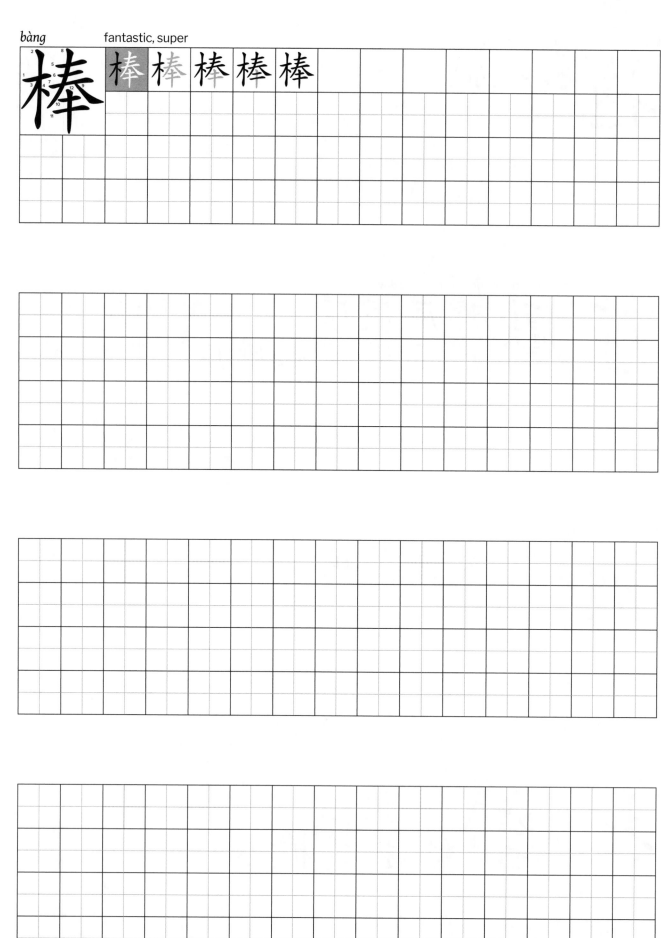

Lesson 19: Travel

sī to take charge of

司　司　司　司　司　司

shí solid; reality

实　實　实　实　实
實　實　實　實　實　實　實

jì to count; idea

计　計　计　计　计
計　計　計

huà plan

划　劃　划　划　划　划　划　划
劃　劃　劃　劃　劃

fù　　father

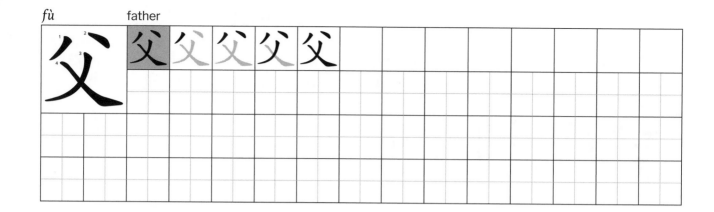

mǔ　　mother

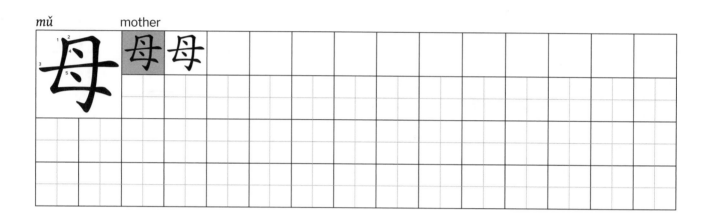

shǒu　　head

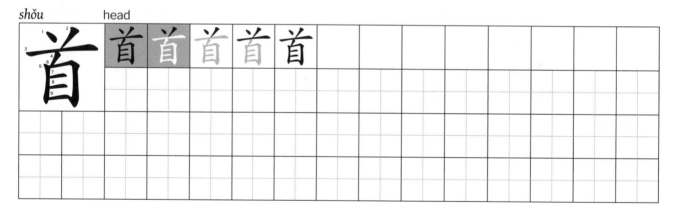

zhèng　　politics

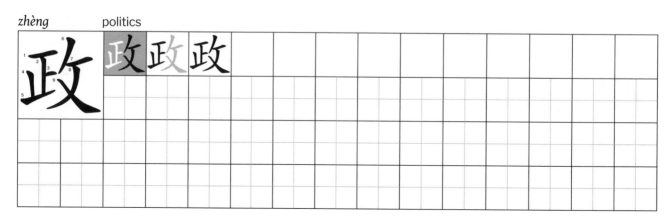

zhì to govern, to manage

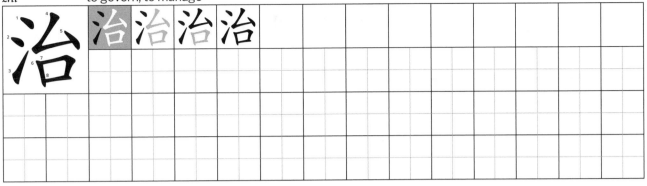

huà to transform, to influence

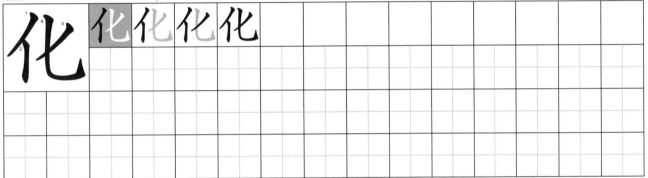

shèng victory; wonderful

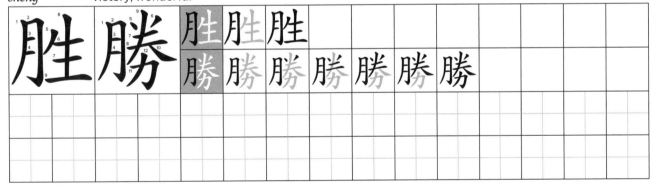

gǔ ancient

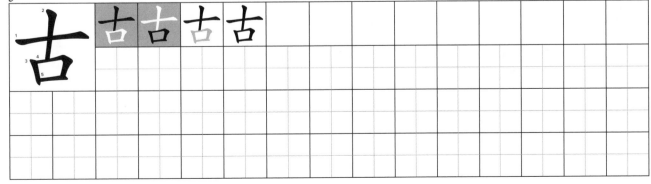

jì　　　　remains, ruins

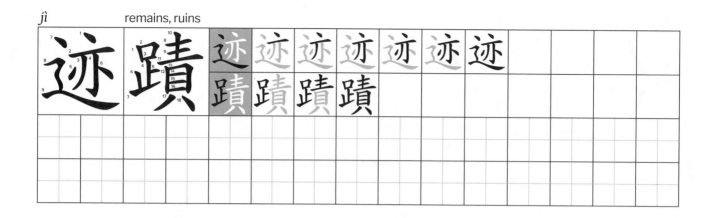

dǎo　　　　to lead, to guide

yóu　　　　遊: to swim, to rove around; 遊: to roam, to travel

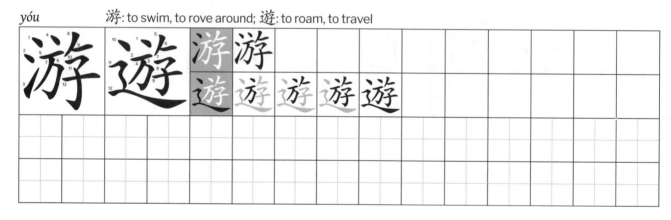

hù　　　　to protect

qiān   to sign

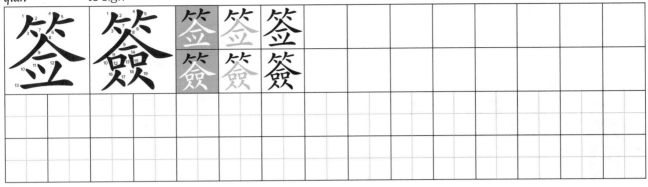

zhèng   proof, certificate

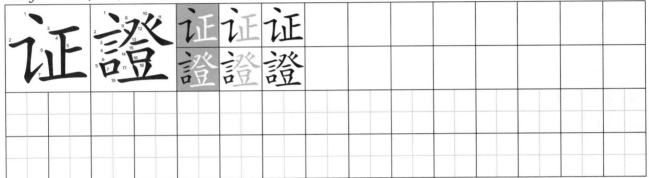

shè   organized body

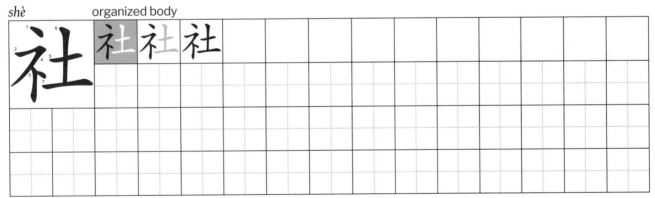

dìng   to reserve, to book (a ticket, a hotel room, etc.)

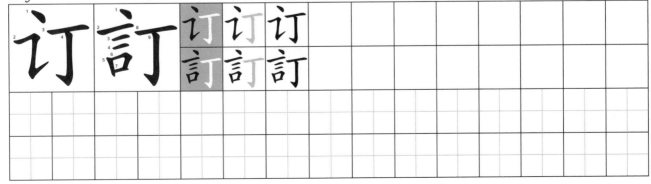

xiāng fragrant

香　香 香 香 香

gǎng harbor

港　港 港 港 港 港 港

tái platform, deck

台　台 台 台

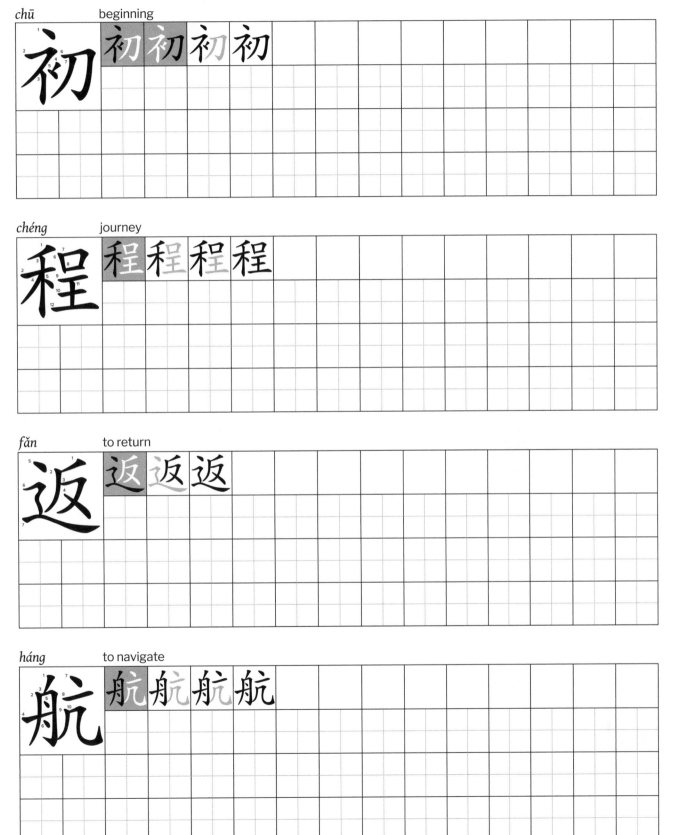

chū beginning

初 初 初 初 初

chéng journey

程 程 程 程 程

fǎn to return

返 返 返 返

háng to navigate

航 航 航 航 航

qiān   thousand

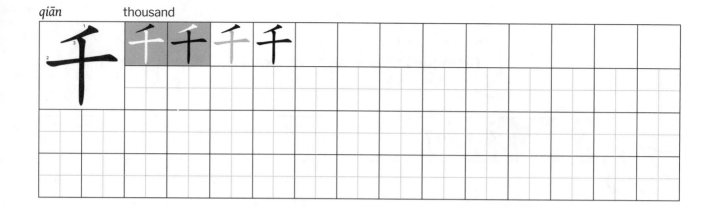

zhé   to fold

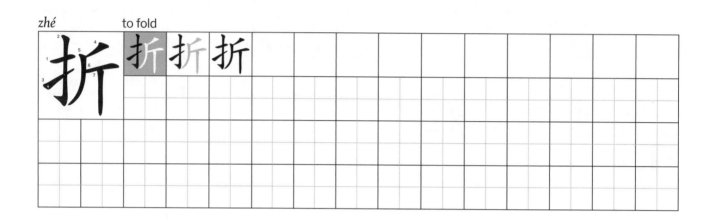

zhuǎn   to turn

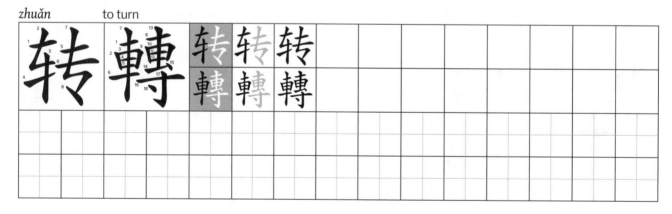

kào   to lean on, to lean against, to be next to

chuāng window

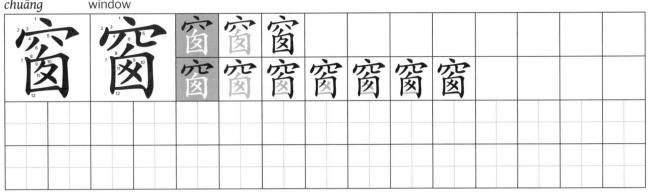

hù door

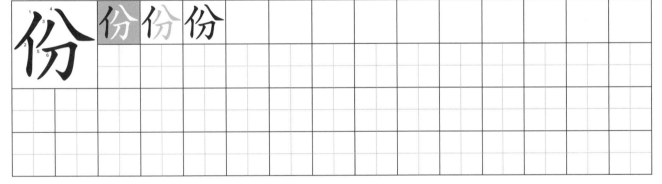

fèn (measure word for meal orders, jobs)

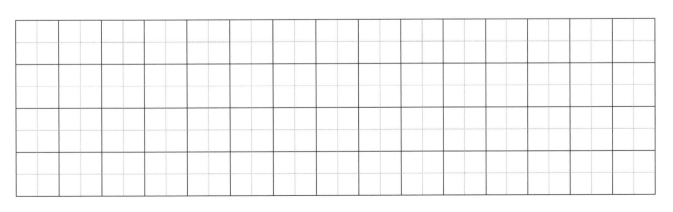

Lesson 20: At the Airport

tuō　　to entrust

托　托 托 托 托 托

bāo　　bag, sack, bundle, package

包　包 包 包

chāo　　to exceed, to surpass

超　超 超 超 超

dēng　　to climb, to ascend

登　登 登 登

pái   plate, tablet, card

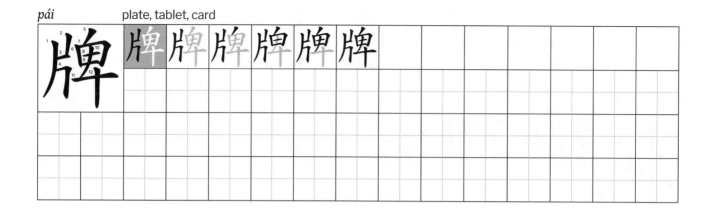

kū   to cry, to weep

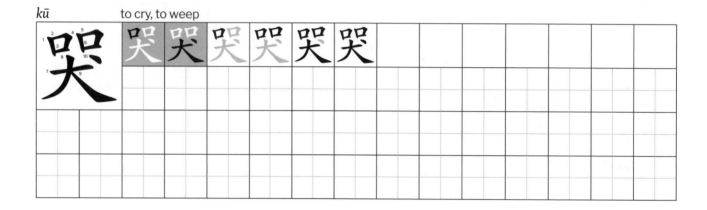

gù   to look after, to attend to

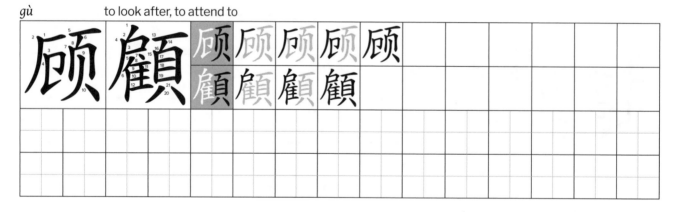

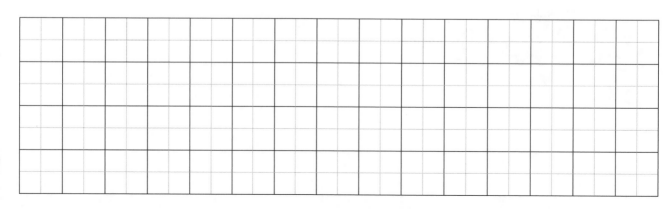

Dialogue 2: Arriving in Beijing

shū uncle

叔　叔 叔 叔 叔

ā (a prefix)

阿 阿　阿 阿 阿 阿 阿
阿 阿 阿 阿 阿

yí aunt

姨　姨 姨 姨 姨 姨 姨

yíng to welcome

迎　迎 迎 迎 迎 迎

shòu   thin, skinny, lean

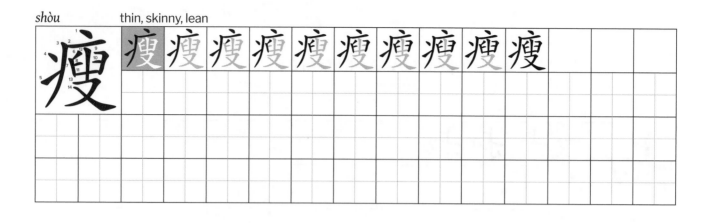

yé   paternal grandfather; (respectful form of address for an elderly man)

nǎi   milk

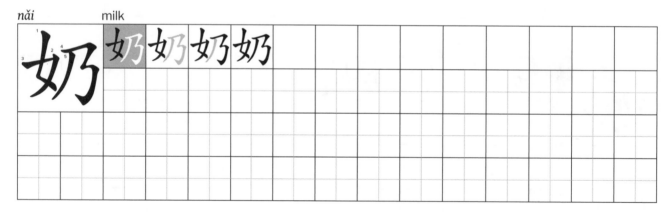

kǎo   to bake, to roast, to grill

yā　　　duck

鴨 鴨 鴨 鴨 鴨 鴨 鴨 鴨 鴨
鴨 鴨 鴨 鴨 鴨 鴨 鴨 鴨 鴨 鴨

INDEX A

Some simplified and traditional characters that appear identical are technically considered to have a different number of strokes. When this is the case, we present the stroke orders for both the simplified and traditional versions of the character to highlight this difference.

P	S	T	Definition	L	Page
dēng	登		to climb, to ascend	20	79
dìng	定		settled, decided	14	36
dìng	订	訂	to reserve, to book (a ticket, a hotel room, etc.)	19	73
dōng	冬		winter	11	5
dòng	动	動	to move	13	23
dòu	豆		bean	12	10
dù	肚		belly, abdomen	15	39
è	饿	餓	hungry	12	15
ér	而		(component in 而且)	11	3
fǎn	返		to return	19	75
fáng	房		house	16	50
fàng	放		to put, to place	12	11
fēi	非		not, non-	11	5
fèi	费	費	to spend, to take (effort)	16	48
fèn	份		(measure word for meal order, job)	19	77
fǔ	腐		rotten; turn bad	12	11
fù	傅		teacher, instructor	12	17
fù	附	附	to attach; near	17	51
fù	父		father	19	70
gāi	该	該	should, ought to	18	66
gān	干	乾	dry	17	55
gǎn	感		to feel, to sense	15	43
gǎn	赶	趕	to rush	15	45
gāng	刚	剛	just now, a moment ago	11	2
gǎng	港		harbor	19	74
gāo	糕		cake	11	5
gèng	更		even more	11	3
gǒu	狗		dog	14	34
gòu	够	夠	enough	12	14
gǔ	谷		grain, valley	13	27
gǔ	古		ancient	19	71
gù	顾	顧	to look after, to attend to	20	80

P	S	T	Definition	L	Page
guā	瓜		melon, gourd	12	19
guǎi	拐	拐	to turn	13	26
guān	关	關	to involve, to close	12	21
guǎng	广	廣	wide, vast	17	51
háng	航		to navigate	19	75
hù	护	護	to protect	19	72
hù	户		door	19	77
huá	滑	滑	slippery; to slide	11	1
huà	划	劃	plan	19	69
huà	化		to transform, to influence	19	71
huài	坏	壞	bad	15	41
huó	活		to live; living	13	24
jí	极	極	extremely	12	18
jì	记	記	to remember	16	49
jì	际	際	border, boundary	18	65
jì	计	計	to count; idea	19	69
jì	迹	蹟	remains, ruins	19	72
jiā	加		to add	11	7
jiā	家	傢	家: family, home; 傢: furniture	17	53
jià	架		shelf	17	56
jiǎn	检	檢	to inspect, to examine	15	41
jiǎn	简	簡	simple	18	61
jiàn	健		healthy	15	44
jiǎo	饺	餃	dumpling	12	10
jiǎo	脚	腳	foot	18	66
jiē	接		to catch, to meet, to welcome	14	31
jīng	精		essence; refined	12	13
jīng	睛		eyeball	14	35
jìng	净	淨	clean	17	55
jìng	静	靜	quiet	17	56
jù	具	俱	具: tool, utensil; 俱: all, complete; altogether	17	53

P	S	T	Definition	L	Page
kāng	康		healthy, affluent	15	44
kǎo	烤		to bake, to roast, to grill	20	82
kào	靠		to lean on, to lean against, to be next to	19	76
kě	渴		thirsty	12	14
kū	哭		to cry, to weep	20	80
là	辣		spicy, hot	12	12
lán	篮	籃	basket	18	63
lǎn	懒	懶	lazy	15	46
lěng	冷		cold	11	2
lí	离	離	away from	13	24
lí	梨		pear	14	31
lǐ	礼	禮	gift, ceremony	14	29
lǐ	理		reason; in good order	16	50
liǎ	俩	倆	(coll.) two	16	48
lián	连	連	even	17	51
liǎn	脸	臉	face	14	34
liáng	凉	涼	cool	12	19
liào	料		material	14	30
lìng	另		other, another	17	58
lóu	楼	樓	multi-story building, floor (of a multi-level building)	14	32
lǚ	旅		to travel	16	50
luàn	乱	亂	randomly, arbitrarily, messily	15	46
lún	伦	倫	ethics, moral principles	14	37
mǎ	码	碼	(symbol indicating a number)	16	49
mài	卖	賣	to sell	12	13
mào	冒		to belch, to emit	15	43
mǐ	米		uncooked rice	12	19
mín	民		the people	17	57
mǐn	敏		nimble, agile	15	44
mǔ	姆		housemaid	14	37
mǔ	母		mother	19	70

P	S	T	Definition	L	Page
ná	拿		to take, to get	13	25
nǎi	奶		milk	20	82
nán	南		south	13	26
niú	牛		cow, ox	12	18
nuǎn	暖		warm	11	3
pà	怕		to fear, to be afraid of	18	61
pāi	拍		racket	18	62
pái	牌		plate, tablet, card	20	80
pán	盘	盤	plate, dish	12	10
páng	旁		side, edge	13	23
pàng	胖		fat	18	61
pǎo	跑		to run	18	62
piàn	片		(measure word for tablets, slices, etc.)	15	42
píng	苹	蘋	(component in 苹果/蘋果)	14	30
qiān	签	簽	to sign	19	73
qiān	千		thousand	19	76
qiě	且		(component in 而且)	11	3
qīng	青		blue, green	12	14
qīng	清		pure, clear	12	20
qiū	秋		autumn, fall	11	6
qù	趣		interest, delight, aspiration	17	59
rè	热	熱	hot	11	6
ròu	肉		meat	12	11
sài	赛	賽	game, match, competition	18	65
sǎo	扫	掃	to sweep	16	49
shā	沙		sand	17	55
shāo	烧	燒	to burn	12	18
shè	社		organized body	19	73
shēn	身		body	15	43
shèng	胜	勝	victory, wonderful	19	71
shí	实	實	solid; reality	19	69

P	S	T	Definition	L	Page
shì	式		type, style	18	65
shǒu	首		head	19	70
shòu	受		to bear	18	62
shòu	瘦		thin, skinny, lean	20	82
shū	舒		relax, comfortable	11	7
shū	叔		uncle	20	81
shǔ	暑		heat	14	33
shǔ	属	屬	to belong to	14	34
sī	司		to take charge of	19	69
sǐ	死		to die; (a complement indicating an extreme degree)	15	40
sù	素		vegetarian (lit. plain)	12	10
suān	酸		sour	12	12
tái	台		platform, deck	19	74
tāng	汤	湯	soup	12	12
táng	糖		sugar	12	17
tǎng	躺		to lie, to recline	15	41
tào	套		(measure word for things that come in a set or sets)	17	52
téng	疼		to ache	15	39
tī	踢		to kick	18	66
tí	提		to lift	18	65
tǐ	体	體	body	15	43
tián	甜		sweet	12	18
tóu	头	頭	head	14	33
tuō	托		to entrust	20	79
wán	完		finished	12	13
wǎn	碗		bowl	12	11
wǎng	往		towards	13	26
wàng	忘		to forget	12	20
wēi	危		danger	18	63
wèi	味		flavor, taste	12	12
wèi	卫	衛	to guard, to protect	17	53

P	S	T	Definition	L	Page
wò	卧	臥	to lie (down)	17	52
wù	务	務	affair, task	12	9
wù	物		thing, matter	14	29
xī	息		to cease	15	46
xì	系	係	to relate to	12	21
xià	夏		summer	11	6
xiǎn	险	險	risk, danger	15	45
xiāng	箱		box, case	15	40
xiāng	香		fragrant	19	74
xiàng	像	像	likeness, portrait	12	9
xiàng	象	象	appearance, shape	16	47
xiē	些		(measure word for an indefinite amount), some	12	14
xiū	休		to cease	15	46
xuě	雪		snow	11	1
yā	押		to give as security	17	57
yā	压	壓	to press, to hold down, to weigh down	18	67
yā	鸭	鴨	duck	20	83
yān	淹		to submerge	18	64
yán	盐	鹽	salt	12	13
yǎn	眼		eye	14	35
yǎn	演		to show (a film), to perform	16	47
yǎng	痒	癢	itchy	15	44
yǎng	养	養	to raise	17	58
yào	药	藥	medicine	15	42
yé	爷	爺	paternal grandfather, (respectful form of address for an elderly man)	20	82
yè	夜		night	15	40
yí	姨		aunt	20	81
yǐ	椅		chair	17	55
yǐn	饮	飲	to drink	14	30
yìn	印		to print	16	47

INDEX B

Characters by Lesson and Pinyin

P	S	T	Definition	L	Page
wǎn	碗		bowl	12	11
wàng	忘		to forget	12	20
wèi	味		flavor, taste	12	12
wù	务	務	affair, task	12	9
xì	系	係	to relate to	12	21
xiàng	像	像	likeness, portrait	12	9
xiē	些		(measure word for an indefinite amount), some	12	14
yán	盐	鹽	salt	12	13
yú	鱼	魚	fish	12	17
zhuō	桌		table	12	9
āi	哎	哎	(exclamatory particle to express surprise or dissatisfaction)	13	26
cì	次		(measure word for frequency)	13	25
cóng	从	從	from	13	25
dēng	灯	燈	light	13	27
dòng	动	動	to move	13	23
gǔ	谷		grain, valley	13	27
guǎi	拐	拐	to turn	13	26
huó	活		to live; living	13	24
lí	离	離	away from	13	24
ná	拿		to take, to get	13	25
nán	南		south	13	26
páng	旁		side, edge	13	23
wǎng	往		towards	13	26
yòu	右		right	13	27
yuǎn	远	遠	far	13	23
yùn	运	運	to move	13	23
zhí	直		straight	13	25
zuǒ	左		left	13	27
bǎ	把		(measure word for things with handles, for handfuls of things)	14	30
bān	班		class	14	34
běn	本		(measure word for books)	14	29
bí	鼻		nose	14	35
biǎo	表		(component in 表姐)	14	29
cōng	聪	聰	able to hear well	14	33
dàn	蛋		egg	14	36
dìng	定		settled, decided	14	36
gǒu	狗		dog	14	34
jiē	接		to catch, to meet, to welcome	14	31
jīng	睛		eyeball	14	35
lí	梨		pear	14	31
lǐ	礼	禮	gift, ceremony	14	29
liǎn	脸	臉	face	14	34
liào	料		material	14	30
lóu	楼	樓	multi-story building, floor (of a multi-level building)	14	32
lún	伦	倫	ethics, moral principles	14	37
mǔ	姆		housemaid	14	37
píng	苹	蘋	(component in 苹果/蘋果)	14	30
shǔ	暑		heat	14	33
shǔ	属	屬	to belong to	14	34
tóu	头	頭	head	14	33
wù	物		thing, matter	14	29
yǎn	眼		eye	14	35
yǐn	饮	飲	to drink	14	30
yuán	圆	圓	round	14	35
zhōng	钟	鐘	clock	14	33
zhòng	重		heavy, serious	14	31
zhù	住		to live (in a certain place)	14	31
zuǐ	嘴		mouth	14	36
bǎo	保		insurance, to protect	15	45
biàn	遍		(measure word for complete courses of an action or instances of an action)	15	42

P	S	T	Definition	L	Page
bìng	病		illness; to become ill	15	39
cè	厕	廁	toilet	15	40
chá	查		to look up	15	41
dù	肚		belly, abdomen	15	39
gǎn	感		to feel, to sense	15	43
gǎn	赶	趕	to rush	15	45
huài	坏	壞	bad	15	41
jiǎn	检	檢	to inspect, to examine	15	41
jiàn	健		healthy	15	44
kāng	康		healthy, affluent	15	44
lǎn	懒	懶	lazy	15	46
luàn	乱	亂	randomly, arbitrarily, messily	15	46
mào	冒		to belch, to emit	15	43
mǐn	敏		nimble, agile	15	44
piàn	片		(measure word for tablets, slices, etc.)	15	42
shēn	身		body	15	43
sǐ	死		to die; (a complement indicating an extreme degree)	15	40
tǎng	躺		to lie, to recline	15	41
téng	疼		to ache	15	39
tǐ	体	體	body	15	43
xī	息		to cease	15	46
xiǎn	险	險	risk, danger	15	45
xiāng	箱		box, case	15	40
xiū	休		to cease	15	46
yǎng	痒	癢	itchy	15	44
yào	药	藥	medicine	15	42
yè	夜		night	15	40
yuàn	院	院	yard, compound	15	39
yuè	越		to exceed	15	45
zhēn	针	針	needle	15	42
bān	搬		to move	16	49

P	S	T	Definition	L	Page
chéng	成		to become	16	47
fáng	房		house	16	50
fèi	费	費	to spend, to take (effort)	16	48
jì	记	記	to remember	16	49
lǐ	理		reason; in good order	16	50
liǎ	俩	倆	(coll.) two	16	48
lǚ	旅		to travel	16	50
mǎ	码	碼	(symbol indicating a number)	16	49
sǎo	扫	掃	to sweep	16	49
xiàng	象	象	appearance, shape	16	47
yǎn	演		to show (a film), to perform	16	47
yìn	印		to print	16	47
zhěng	整		to put in order	16	50
ān	安		calm; at ease	17	56
bì	币	幣	currency	17	57
chà	差	差	to fall short of	17	57
chǎo	吵		to quarrel; noisy	17	51
chǒng	宠	寵	to dote on, to pamper	17	59
chú	厨	廚	kitchen	17	52
dāng	当	當	to serve as, to be	17	58
fù	附	附	to attach; near	17	51
gān	干	乾	dry	17	55
guǎng	广	廣	wide, vast	17	51
jiā	家	傢	家: family, home; 傢: furniture	17	53
jià	架		shelf	17	56
jìng	净	淨	clean	17	55
jìng	静	靜	quiet	17	56
jù	具	俱	具: tool, utensil; 俱: all, complete; altogether	17	53
lián	连	連	even	17	51
lìng	另		other, another	17	58

P	S	T	Definition	L	Page
mín	民		the people	17	57
qù	趣		interest, delight, aspiration	17	59
shā	沙		sand	17	55
tào	套		(measure word for things that come in a set or sets)	17	52
wèi	卫	衛	to guard, to protect	17	53
wò	卧	臥	to lie (down)	17	52
yā	押		to give as security	17	57
yǎng	养	養	to raise	17	58
yǐ	椅		chair	17	55
yù	寓		dwelling, residence	17	52
yuán	元		(measure word for the basic Chinese monetary unit), yuan	17	56
zhǔn	准		to allow, to be allowed	17	58
bàng	棒		fantastic, super	18	67
bào	抱		to hold or carry in the arms	18	67
bèi	被		by	18	67
bù	步		step, pace	18	62
dān	单	單	single	18	61
dān	担	擔	to be burdened with	18	67
gāi	该	該	should, ought to	18	66
jì	际	際	border, boundary	18	65
jiǎn	简	簡	simple	18	61
jiǎo	脚	腳	foot	18	66
lán	篮	籃	basket	18	63
pà	怕		to fear, to be afraid of	18	61
pāi	拍		racket	18	62
pàng	胖		fat	18	61
pǎo	跑		to run	18	62
sài	赛	賽	game, match, competition	18	65
shì	式		type, style	18	65
shòu	受		to bear	18	62

P	S	T	Definition	L	Page
tī	踢		to kick	18	66
tí	提		to lift	18	65
wēi	危		danger	18	63
yā	压	壓	to press, to hold down, to weigh down	18	67
yān	淹		to submerge	18	64
yīng	应	應	should, ought to	18	66
yǒng	泳		swimming	18	63
yóu	游		to swim, to rove around	18	63
yuàn	愿	願	wish, hope	18	64
chéng	程		journey	19	75
chū	初		beginning	19	75
chuāng	窗	窗	window	19	77
dǎo	导	導	to lead, to guide	19	72
dìng	订	訂	to reserve, to book (a ticket, a hotel room, etc.)	19	73
fǎn	返		to return	19	75
fèn	份		(measure word for meal order, job)	19	77
fù	父		father	19	70
gǎng	港		harbor	19	74
gǔ	古		ancient	19	71
háng	航		to navigate	19	75
hù	护	護	to protect	19	72
hù	户		door	19	77
huà	划	劃	plan	19	69
huà	化		to transform, to influence	19	71
jì	计	計	to count; idea	19	69
jì	迹	蹟	remains, ruins	19	72
kào	靠		to lean on, to lean against, to be next to	19	76
mǔ	母		mother	19	70
qiān	签	簽	to sign	19	73
qiān	千		thousand	19	76
shè	社		organized body	19	73

P	S	T	Definition	L	Page
shèng	胜	勝	victory, wonderful	19	71
shí	实	實	solid; reality	19	69
shǒu	首		head	19	70
sī	司		to take charge of	19	69
tái	台		platform, deck	19	74
xiāng	香		fragrant	19	74
yóu	游		游: to swim, to rove around; 遊: to roam, to travel	19	72
zhé	折		to fold	19	76
zhèng	政		politics	19	70
zhèng	证	證	proof, certificate	19	73
zhì	治		to govern, to manage	19	71
zhuǎn	转	轉	to turn	19	76
ā	阿	阿	(a prefix)	20	81
bāo	包		bag, sack, bundle, package	20	79

P	S	T	Definition	L	Page
chāo	超		to exceed, to surpass	20	79
dēng	登		to climb, to ascend	20	79
gù	顾	顧	to look after, to attend to	20	80
kǎo	烤		to bake, to roast, to grill	20	82
kū	哭		to cry, to weep	20	80
nǎi	奶		milk	20	82
pái	牌		plate, tablet, card	20	80
shòu	瘦		thin, skinny, lean	20	82
shū	叔		uncle	20	81
tuō	托		to entrust	20	79
yā	鸭	鴨	duck	20	83
yé	爷	爺	paternal grandfather, (respectful form of address for an elderly man)	20	82
yí	姨		aunt	20	81
yíng	迎		to welcome	20	81